SRA
# FLEX
LITERACY™

# INTERACTIVE READER
# VOLUME B

## Secondary System

### Authors
Nancy E. Marchand-Martella
Ronald C. Martella
Douglas Fisher
Jay McTighe
Marcia Kosanovich
Mina Johnson-Glenberg
Ernest Morrell

McGraw Hill **Education**

*Bothell, WA • Chicago, IL • Columbus, OH • New York, NY*

**www.*FLEX*Literacy.com**

 **Education**

Send all inquiries to:
McGraw-Hill Education
8787 Orion Place
Columbus, OH  43240

ISBN: 978-0-07-661561-2
MHID: 0-07-661561-8

Printed in the United States of America.

1 2 3 4 5 6 7 8 9 QDB 17 16 15 14 13 12

# Contents

# Contents

# Wringer
## Part One

By Jerry Spinelli

## Build Background

1

**Word:**
.............................
**Definition:**
.............................
.............................
.............................
.............................

**Word:**
.............................
**Definition:**
.............................
.............................
.............................

He did not want to be a wringer.

This was one of the first things he had learned about himself. He could not have said exactly when he learned it, but it was very early. And more than early, it was deep inside.

So it was never gone.

In fact, gone was something it could not be, for he could not escape it any more than he could escape himself. The best he could do was forget it.

But this thing did not like to be forgotten. Like air escaping a **punctured** tire, it would spread out from his stomach and be everywhere.

Just to remind him.

It was simply, merely there, a whisper of feather wings, reminding him of the moment he dreaded above all others, the moment when the not wanting to be a wringer would turn to becoming one.

In his dreams the moment had already come. In his dreams he looks down to find his hands around the neck of the pigeon. It feels silky. The pigeon's eye is like a polished shirt button. The pigeon's eye is orange with a smaller black button in the center. It looks up at him. It does not blink.

He cannot. He cannot wring it, nor can he let go. He wants to let go, **desperately,** but his fingers are

## Generate Questions

.............................................................
.............................................................
.............................................................
.............................................................
.............................................................

stone. And the voices chant: "Wring it! Wring it!" and the orange eye stares.

Palmer's first Pigeon Day had occurred when he was four. Certain moments, five years later, were still with him. The birds in the sky, then suddenly not in the sky, only feathers fluttering.

And most of all the pigeon, the one pigeon that hurried across the grass lopsided—"loppysided," as Palmer would have said then—as if one leg had been kicked out from under it, hurrying, hobbling, wobbling in goofy loops, tilting like a sailboat blown over, a boy chasing after, running and reaching, the boy laughing, the people laughing, little Palmer thinking, *The boy wants it for a pet.* And then the pigeon was coming this way, flopping, righting itself, hobbling straight for the people, head bobbing, loppysiding on a curving course, and the people were shrieking and calling "Wringer! Wringer!" and the boy was chasing and sure enough the boy caught it, caught that hobbly-wobbling pigeon right in front of Palmer. And the pigeon's eye looked at Palmer and the pigeon's eye was orange and everyone clapped and Palmer clapped too and laughed and called out "Good!" and the boy closed his hands over the pigeon's neck and twisted his hands real quick—like *that*—and Palmer heard a tiny sound, like when a twig was stepped on, and when the boy took one hand away the pigeon's head hung down, though the pigeon's eye was still round and orange.

Make Prediction

**Word:** ..........................................................

**Definition:** ..................................................

..........................................................................

..........................................................................

..........................................................................

**Word:** ..........................................................

**Definition:** ..................................................

..........................................................................

..........................................................................

..........................................................................

Palmer had turned and looked up at his mother and said, "Why did he do that?" and his mother had said, "To put the pigeon out of its **misery.**"

"Was the pigeon in misery?" Palmer asked his mother.

"Yes," she said.

"Why?" said Palmer.

His mother did not answer. She was looking at the sky.

"Because he was loppysided?"

She smiled thinly; she nodded. "Yes."

"The boy didn't want him for a pet, did he?"

Suddenly his mother grabbed his hand and pulled him away.

During the following year Palmer thought about that quite often. If the wounded pigeons were in misery, he wondered, why put them there in the first place by shooting them. Why not just let them all fly away?

How sad, to be a pigeon. And how nice of the people, that they would stop at nothing to help. Heaven, Palmer thought with a smile, must be **teeming** with pigeons.

## Generate Questions

..........................................................................

..........................................................................

..........................................................................

..........................................................................

But the questions did not stop. Killing the pigeons and putting them out of their misery stubbornly refused to mean the same thing. Palmer thought about misery, and it seemed to him that a shotgun was not the only way to end it. When Palmer was miserable, for example, his mother or father would hold him close and wipe his tears. When Palmer's mother or father put him out of his misery, they did not shoot him, they offered him a cookie. Why then on Pigeon Day did the people bring guns instead of cookies?

It was confusing.

"Was Daddy a wringer?" Palmer asked his mother one day.

After a minute she said, "Better ask your father."

So he asked his father. "Daddy, were you a wringer?"

His father looked at him and said, "Yep."

"Will I be a wringer too?"

His father gave a snappy nod and said, "Sure thing, big guy."

*Sure thing.* Palmer pronounced the words over and over in the days that followed. *Sure thing.*

Boys became wringers, he heard, when they became ten years old.

## Verify Prediction

◯ CORRECT

◯ INCORRECT

## Summarize

...................................................................................................

...................................................................................................

...................................................................................................

...................................................................................................

...................................................................................................

**Word 1**

**Definition**

**Word 2**

**Definition**

**Word 3**

**Definition**

**Word 4**

**Definition**

| | Active Participation | Interactive Reader | Critical Thinking Application | Week 1 Total |
|---|---|---|---|---|
| **TOTAL POINTS FOR WEEK 1** | | | | |

# Wringer
## Part Two

By Jerry Spinelli

## Build Background

By the following year Palmer no longer cared to watch. So he spent Pigeon Day at the playground with Dorothy Gruzik. Through the day the squeak of the seesaw and the creak of the swings joined the sound of the shotguns.

While they were on the swings, a boy he knew as Arthur Dodds came by. Arthur had not yet begun calling himself Beans.

"Whattya doing?" he demanded of the two of them.

"We're swinging," said Dorothy. "What's it look like?"

"They're shooting the pigeons," he said. "Come on!"

"We're staying here," said Dorothy.

Palmer was glad that Dorothy answered, but now Arthur Dodds was heading straight for him.

"You coming?" he said.

Palmer did not know what to say. He looked at Dorothy. He shook his head no.

Arthur Dodds exploded. He gave the swing chain such a yank that Palmer was thrown like a bronco rider onto the ground. Arthur Dodds took off, **braying,** "I'm a wringer, I'm a wringer! I'm gonna get me a pigeon and wring 'im!"

And he did.

## Generate Questions

As Palmer later heard the story, Arthur Dodds made a real nuisance of himself on that day. He kept darting onto the field to chase wounded pigeons, only to be chased away himself by the real wringers.

A shot bird, instead of falling onto the soccer field, made it to the picnic area before it came down. Arthur saw and **lit** out after it. He heard a woman screaming. The bird had fallen right into the pink-fringed stroller where her baby was sleeping.

By the time Arthur got there, the pigeon was on the ground and being chased around the picnic tables by half a dozen squealing toddlers. Arthur joined the chase. The bird flapped up onto a table. Arthur lunged across the table, knocking drinks, smashing pickled eggs, and snatched the pigeon by the legs in a bowl of chicken salad. According to the story, Arthur threw his arms into the air like a boxing champion and crowed, "Got me one!" Then, right before the gaping eyes of the picnickers, he wrung its neck.

So proud was he of his dead pigeon that he took it home, wrapped it in newspaper and hid it under his bed. For almost a week he charged kids a quarter apiece for a look. Then his mother started to smell something, and pretty soon that was that.

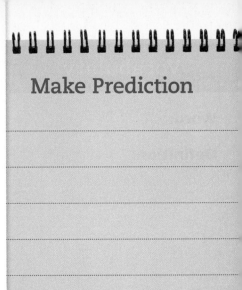

## Make Prediction

Arthur Dodds became Beans, and Beans was joined by Billy Natola, who became Mutto, and by a new, very tall boy in town known only as Henry. Palmer wanted to join them, but they said he was too small and too young and that he had a funny first name and that he played with girls, little ones at that.

In second grade he said to the guys, "She's my neighbor, that's all. I can't help that, can I? And anyway, what do I want with a first grader?" But they weren't listening.

That was the summer that Palmer's family went on a vacation trip. They stopped in the big city for a day.

Pigeons were everywhere: sidewalks, ledges, steps. Palmer even saw one crossing a street with a crowd of people on a green light, just another pedestrian. They **strutted** boldly, those pigeons, going about their business, pecking here, pecking there. They acted as if they belonged, as if this was their city as well as the people's.

Palmer kept tugging at his parents: "Look, there's one! . . . Look at that one!" But the city people ignored them. No one had a shotgun.

## Generate Questions

Except for a wounded pigeon that was wrung in front of him when he was four, this was Palmer's first close look at the birds. He had heard that pigeons were dirty, filthy, nothing more than rats with wings. He looked and looked, but all he saw were plump, pretty birds with shiny coats. They did not hop, like sparrows or robins, but they *walked,* one pink foot in front of the other, just like people. With each step the head gave a nod, as if to say, *Yes, I will. I agree. You're right.* As Palmer saw it, the pigeon was a most agreeable bird.

It was about then that Palmer began to feel a certain **tilt** to his life. Time became a sliding board, at the bottom of which awaited his tenth birthday.

Beans kept asking, "You gonna be a wringer?"

Every time, Palmer would look straight into that crayon box of teeth and say, "Sure thing." And every time he said it he could feel his heart thump. For among all the changes in his life, one thing stayed the same. It was something he had known since his second Pigeon Day, when he sat with Dorothy Gruzik on the swings: He did not want to be a wringer.

## Verify Prediction

○ CORRECT

○ INCORRECT

## Summarize

....................................................................................................

....................................................................................................

....................................................................................................

....................................................................................................

....................................................................................................

**Sentence** I set my skateboard at a        against the wall.

**Sentence** The cowboy        up to the sheriff and said, "I'm not going anywhere."

**Sentence** Jenn knew she was in trouble, so she      out of the room.

**Sentence** The little boy ran around the room,        after his finger was slammed in the door.

| | Active Participation | Interactive Reader | Critical Thinking Application | Week 2 Total |
|---|---|---|---|---|
| **TOTAL POINTS FOR WEEK 2** | | | | |

# Wringer
## Part Three

By Jerry Spinelli

## Build Background

Cotton candy days, Ferris wheel nights. Family Fest was almost better than Christmas—and longer. What had been the American Legion baseball field last week was this week a wonderland. Ten times over Palmer explored every ride, every food stand, every amusement booth. He loved the **yelp** and splash when a ball hit the mark at the Dunk-A-Kid booth, the pop of darted balloons, the St. Bernard-size grand prizes, Tilt-A-Whirl's woozy flight, neon lights like bottled fireworks, House of Horrors and Pretzel Man and chocolate bananas on a stick.

But in this year of Palmer's life not even Family Fest was pure and easy fun. Despite the gleeful shouting and merry-go-round music, he could not forget the soccer field at the far end of the park: silent, waiting. At times the Ferris wheel seemed to be **winching** minutes, hauling him ever closer to Saturday and the boom and smell of gun smoke.

He tried to avoid the guys, but it wasn't as easy as before. They were supposed to meet at the World War I cannon. The shooting would begin at seven and continue all day.

When he was younger this was a matter of wonderment to Palmer. It became the means by which he could grasp the first really big number in his life: five thousand. For a time five thousand meant the number of pigeons you could shoot in one day, one by one.

## Generate Questions

"Why don't you just blow them up and put them out of their misery all at once?" he asked his father one day.

That was when his father explained how it all worked. He explained that there was more to it than putting the pigeons out of their misery. He said that only people who paid money were allowed to shoot the pigeons, and that the money was used to make the park better. "So you see," he said, "you can thank a pigeon for the swings at the playground."

And for a time thereafter, Palmer did just that. Whenever he swung on a swing, he thanked a pigeon.

When he went to bed Friday night he had decided what he would do: He would not show up at the cannon. If they came checking, he would be in bed, pretending to be sick.

He felt good. The problem was solved. He went to sleep with a smile.

In his dream the pigeons came to town, not five thousand but millions. In their beaks they pinched the edges of the town, plucked it up and flew away with it, as if it were a Christmas tree display on a tablecloth. On and on they flew.

## Make Prediction

He opened his eyes. The light was blinding, then went away. It was totally dark. The nightlight was off, and he was not alone in bed. *Somebody was in bed with him!* He started to make a sound, but his mouth was clamped by a hand. Somebody laughed out loud, somebody growled, "Shut up! They'll hear!" The light reappeared. It was a little penlight. It shone on two faces. One of them said, "Shut up now, Snots, okay? It's just us, Beans and Mutto. Okay?"

Next thing he knew he was yanked out of bed and onto his feet. "Come on," whispered Beans, "we got somewhere to go."

Once the shock wore off, he realized what an honor had been granted him. Imagine: A month ago these guys ignored him except to tease him; now they snuck into his house and climbed into bed with him, Palmer LaRue. Amazing!

It was not like Palmer to do this. He had always been an **obedient** kid. Lay down a rule, and Palmer followed it. He **cringed** at what his parents would say if they found out.

But the thrill of it, the honor of it swept all other feelings away. He wondered what other adventures awaited him in the days and years ahead.

They trotted through the park and past the National Guard Armory. They turned a corner, and they were at the old boarded-up railroad station. Palmer smelled something, like animals, and heard small, soft sounds.

## Generate Questions

It was five thousand pigeons.

He stopped.

Palmer could not move. Ten thousand orange eyes burned holes in his heart.

He heard a wrenching screech: they were ripping open a crate. What were they up to?

*Ten thousand orange eyes.*

He ran. He did not use the alleys. He ran down the middle of the streets, the middle of the lights, chased every step by the uproar of the crates, ten thousand orange eyes trailing him into his house, into his bed, under his sheet, into his sleep.

In the morning, Saturday morning, awakening, he heard tiny popping sounds in the distance. He closed his window, pulled down the shade.

Blessedly they did not come for him. Still, to be on the safe side, he told his mother he was ill and stayed in bed all day.

Several times, when the light was deeply golden on the window shade, he heard the doorbell downstairs and his mother going to answer. She did not say who was there. He did not ask.

When his mother came in to kiss him goodnight, she turned off the TV and opened the window. The night was silent.

## Verify Prediction

○ CORRECT

○ INCORRECT

## Summarize

..................................................................................................................

..................................................................................................................

..................................................................................................................

..................................................................................................................

..................................................................................................................

**Word 1**

**Sentence**

**Word 2**

**Sentence**

**Word 3**

**Sentence**

**Word 4**

**Sentence**

| | Active Participation | Interactive Reader | Critical Thinking Application | Week 3 Total |
|---|---|---|---|---|
| **TOTAL POINTS FOR WEEK 3** | | | | |

# Sandy Wilson vs. Flesh-Eating Bacteria

By Troy Markham

## Build Background

Our bodies deal with bacterial infection constantly. As bacteria invade us through the air, water, food, and injuries, we often never even notice. Most bacteria are quickly defeated by our immune systems, and we return to full health.

Although bacterial diseases used to cause many deaths throughout history, the invention of antibiotic drugs changed that. With these "weapons", humans gained the edge, and most bacterial pathogens were easily destroyed. In fact, many thought we would never have to worry about bacteria again. But this was not the case. Increasingly, bacterial infections have become more common. Even more alarming, they have become more deadly. The case of Sandy Wilson is one example.

Wilson came down with an infection shortly after giving birth to her son in 2005. At first it was not apparent that there was anything seriously wrong. She was treated for high blood pressure and swelling, then released. But she was quickly back in the hospital, feeling even worse.

It became apparent that the bacterial infection was consuming her body. Doctors put Wilson under **sedation** while they attempted to stop the infection. Antibiotics would not work. They were left with only one option to contain the infection: cutting away the pieces of her body that were infected. But the

## Generate Questions

Sandy Wilson vs. Flesh-eating Bacteria

infection continued to spread. As the bacteria raged along, the horrified staff watched her flesh rapidly rot away in front of their eyes.

When Wilson woke up, she was shocked to see how much of her body was gone. The bacteria had eaten away the skin that covered her lower body. When she looked down, she could see her body's organs beneath a clear wrapping. Unfortunately she was still not well. Doctors attempted more than fifty surgeries, trying desperately to stay ahead of the bacterial decay by cutting away more and more diseased tissue. She remained in the hospital while machines fed her, helped her breathe, and pumped antibiotics and painkillers into her.

Visits from her newborn son gave her emotional strength. Eventually surgeons came up with a plan to **transplant** new organs into her body. The surgery was long and difficult, and her recovery continued to be plagued by the ever-present bacterial infection.

Finally, though, she reached the stage where she was able to eat on her own again. It had been over two years since she had last tasted food. She eagerly devoured a meal of lasagna and salad.

Make Prediction

## Vocabulary

**Word:**
......................................................

**Definition:**
......................................................
......................................................
......................................................
......................................................

**Word:**
......................................................

**Definition:**
......................................................
......................................................
......................................................
......................................................

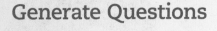

It was too early to celebrate, however. After her meal, Wilson experienced irritation and had to return to getting food through a tube. The taste of food stirred her spirit, though. She fought again to recover. The next time she ate, she ate only small amounts. Eventually she was able to eat full meals again.

Wilson continued to battle the damage caused by the flesh-eating bacteria. Her new body organs began to function. Doctors monitored her progress closely to make sure her body would not reject any of the new organs. They also wanted to make sure her infection did not return.

Her triumph was complete in 2008 when she was finally able to come home from the hospital after almost three years. Finally able to live with her child, who was now no longer a baby, she basked in her return to normalcy. "I am enjoying spending every moment I can at home with my son," she declared.

## Generate Questions

......................................................
......................................................
......................................................
......................................................
......................................................

Sandy Wilson vs. Flesh-eating Bacteria

Ironically the weapon that is most commonly used against bacteria—antibiotics—is what has created the problem we now face. Antibiotics have been so effective in killing bacteria that humans overuse them. Doctors prescribe antibiotics routinely, even when bacteria might not be causing an illness.

When bacteria are exposed to antibiotics, almost all the bacteria are killed. But some are not. The bacteria that survive are **resistant** to the antibiotic. These bacteria reproduce and create more resistant bacteria. As this process repeats, more and more bacteria found in our environment turn out to be resistant to antibiotics. These bacteria are difficult to stop once they infect a person. This makes them especially dangerous.

Flesh-eating bacteria are not only becoming more common, they are becoming more **aggressive** and showing up in different strains of bacteria. Many people who come down with severe infections do not survive. In many cases, the doctors simply cannot contain the damage before it becomes so severe that the victim dies. Although her ordeal was horrifying, Wilson knows she is very lucky to be alive.

Verify Prediction

○ CORRECT

○ INCORRECT

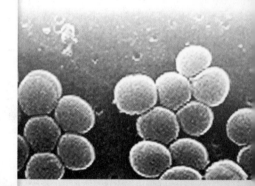

## Summarize

.............................................................................................

.............................................................................................

.............................................................................................

.............................................................................................

.............................................................................................

# Vocabulary Review

## Word 1

**Definition**

## Word 2

**Definition**

## Word 3

**Definition**

## Word 4

**Definition**

| | Active Participation | Interactive Reader | Critical Thinking Application | Week 4 Total |
|---|---|---|---|---|
| **TOTAL POINTS FOR WEEK 4** | | | | |

# THE IDITAROD
## Alaska's Great Race

By Dennis Fertig

## Build Background

It was below ten degrees, but that didn't bother John Baker. After all, March 5 in Anchorage, Alaska, was supposed to be cold! Plus, today's festivities needed frigid weather. So did Baker. He was a musher—a dogsled racer. The festivities were part of the first day of the Iditarod, Alaska's annual 1,100-mile dogsled race.

The crowd and mushers knew today was just the ceremonial first day. The real race would start tomorrow in Willow, Alaska. However, the dogs that pulled the sleds were eager to do what they trained to do: race across the demanding Alaskan landscape.

Dogsleds once had been normal Alaskan transportation. For generations, both natives and people who later immigrated to Alaska depended on dogsleds to **traverse** snow-covered trails. For generations, strong dogs had been bred to pull those sleds.

Eventually motorized transportation eliminated dogsled travel, so the Iditarod race commemorates Alaska's dogsled history. The race also pays tribute to dogs and mushers who once braved a 1925 blizzard to deliver life-saving medicine to isolated Nome, Alaska.

## Generate Questions

The Iditarod: Alaska's Great Race

Baker smiled down at his own dogs. He had competed fifteen times in the **epic** race. Although Baker had never won, last year he had taken fifth. Now, in 2011, he had a great dog team. There were rumors, however, that Baker's team was slow. Baker's smile deepened. He had a secret.

The next day in Willow, each sled was loaded with gear: sleeping bag, ax, snowshoes, cooking equipment, food, headlamps for nighttime, and other things necessary for survival in the desolate Alaskan wilderness. Each musher understood the life-threatening dangers ahead. The race might go through the harshest weather imaginable. Howling winds and below-zero temperatures could drop wind chills to minus-100 degrees. Snow could blind mushers and dogs. And if the weather warmed, ice could weaken over frigid lakes and rivers. In 1984, the great Iditarod musher Susan Butcher had almost died when her team and sled plunged through softening ice into a lake.

As Baker started from Willow, he didn't worry about the Alaskan dangers but about the other mushers. One fierce competitor was Lance Mackey, winner of the last four races. Another was Rick Swenson, who had won five times. Could Baker beat them?

Make Prediction

The Iditarod: Alaska's Great Race

**Word:**

**Definition:**

**Word:**

**Definition:**

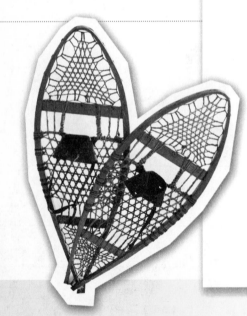

The wide trail from Willow allowed sled teams to **maneuver** for position. Reporters watched and noted many fast dog teams, including Mackey's. Baker's dogs weren't mentioned. That didn't matter to Baker. He still had his secret.

Over the next days, the trail grew narrow and treacherous. Some sleds slid off, and mushers were injured. By the end of the third day, several racers had already dropped out of the race. In all, sixteen wouldn't finish. As mushers dropped out, reporters talked about favorites among those remaining. Baker's name still wasn't mentioned much.

At the end of the fourth day, race leaders were halfway through the 1,100-mile distance. Baker was one of them. He knew that if weather conditions held, this would be a fast race. Still, the toll on Baker and all the mushers was high. Dogs were rotated in and out of teams in order to rest, but mushers raced the whole way, often through exhausting nights. Mushers needed great strength, quick reactions, and unfailing endurance. Iditarod rules required that mushers take set rest times. Even then, mushers got little sleep. They pushed on without real rest for days.

Reporters again discussed teams that seemed strong, and finally Baker got some **recognition.** With good reason—the veteran musher was in second place.

## Generate Questions

The mushers now raced northeast *on* the frozen Yukon River! Baker shocked many and took the lead. As he moved ahead, reporters wondered if other mushers were taking Baker for granted. They had heard his dogs were slow. Were competitors giving him too much of a lead? Maybe Baker's team wasn't as slow as it was rumored.

The trail headed to Unalakleet, a town on the Bering Sea. The first musher there would win $25,000 in gold nuggets. Just before dawn, March 13, Baker claimed that prize!

The trail now followed the frozen Alaskan seacoast. This stretch often broke leads like Baker's. Reporters eyed the fast mushers behind him. They thought Baker might be caught. But still, no one knew Baker's secret.

Over the next days, only one musher still chased Baker—Ramey Smith. Smith had a reputation for speed. Could he catch Baker? On March 15, 2011, Baker answered that question when he was the first to enter Nome, Alaska. He had won in record time!

Reporters asked Baker how people had gotten the idea that his dogs were slow. Baker smiled, and finally his secret was revealed. Baker replied, "Probably from me."

## Summarize

.................................................................................

.................................................................................

.................................................................................

.................................................................................

.................................................................................

**Sentence** The _____ story was long and exciting.

**Sentence** The skier will _____ the mountain to get to the other side.

**Sentence** I had to _____ my car around the fallen tree.

**Sentence** The _____ for performing well on the test felt good to me.

| | Active Participation | Interactive Reader | Critical Thinking Application | Week 5 Total |
|---|---|---|---|---|
| **TOTAL POINTS FOR WEEK 5** | | | | |

# Follow the Water
## . . . To MARS!

By Arden Davidson

## Build Background

It was May 25, 2008. The late afternoon light slanted into the space lab at the University of Arizona in Tucson. The science team had gathered to watch live pictures of the *Phoenix* lander's touchdown on Mars. They knew this robotic spacecraft well. They had helped design and build it. The mission was called "Follow the water." Its goal was to take pictures and to test the hard, dry soil to see if liquid water ever existed there. Mission Control in California counted down as *Phoenix* came feet-first toward the ground. One thousand meters. Five hundred meters. "Touchdown signal acquired!" The room erupted in cheers, hugs, and a few tears. The seven-foot-high robot had finished a 10-month, 423 million-mile journey to Mars. Now it was ready to dig.

Scientists were already sure there was ice on Mars. Pictures from orbiting spacecraft seemed to confirm it. Methane and hydrogen gasses had been detected, so the **inkling** that water ice lay deep underground was a good guess. But had it ever melted? What minerals were in the soil? Had there ever been life on Mars? Scientists from all over the world were excited to find out.

Generate Questions

Follow the Water . . . to Mars!

Two hours later, more cheers erupted when the first pictures came in. They showed *Phoenix* on a rocky, flat plain, right where it was supposed to be. "Even though it looks like a parking lot, it's a perfect place to land," mission director Peter Smith said. The spot in Mars' Arctic plains had been chosen because it was so cold. Researchers hoped to find ice beneath the dry cracked surface.

After the celebration was over, the Arizona team got to work. The team would direct the spacecraft using electronic commands. Soon *Phoenix* was using its eight-foot robotic arm to dig into the planet's surface, dump soil into its tiny oven, and **analyze** the samples. Engineers had equipped *Phoenix* with a powerful microscope and a "chemistry lab in a box" to analyze minerals and gases.

New data and more stunning pictures were posted daily on the Internet, catching the public's interest too. *Phoenix* even had its own Twitter account (a social networking site) with more than 10,000 followers. "Cheers! Tears!! I'm here!" it tweeted. When tiny white chunks in soil samples turned out to be ice, *Phoenix* tweeted, "We have ICE!!!! Yes, ICE, *WATER ICE* on Mars! w00t!!! Best day ever!!" As you might have guessed, the tweets came from a NASA staff member, not the robot. But people were still delighted.

The scientific community was more reserved but clearly **elated.** "It is with great pride and a lot of joy I announce today we have found proof that this . . . is water ice," Smith said. This was a breakthrough, because life as we know it doesn't exist without water.

The University of Arizona team **monitored** the spacecraft for six months, almost three months longer than expected. They knew *Phoenix's* solar panels, which supplied energy to keep it going, would stop working in the harsh Martian winter. *Phoenix* went silent in November 2008, but scientists all over the world had gotten everything they wanted from the mission—and more.

Liquid water can't exist on Mars now, and probably hasn't for millions of years. Mars' atmosphere is too thin, and the cold is too intense. But the Martian dirt that *Phoenix* analyzed told the story of the past and may predict the future. Data from *Phoenix* not only confirmed that water ice is on Mars. It also led Smith and others to believe that the area where *Phoenix* landed had a wetter and warmer climate millions of years ago. Living things might have existed there, even though the team didn't find any living material in the soil. But if it happened once, it could happen again.

## Generate Questions

The "follow the water" mission answered many important questions about the surface and climate of Mars. It also sparked new questions. A big surprise was the discovery of a type of salt in the Martian soil. That might mean it's less likely that life will be found on Mars, or this salt could be an energy source for living things.

Scientists got another surprise: it snows on Mars! The lander's weather instrument discovered snow falling from clouds. Before *Phoenix,* no one knew for sure that it snowed on Mars. Now they do, and the quest for new information continues.

Scientists are a cautious bunch, though. As much as we might like to think that there's life on Mars, there's no evidence yet. There is still much to learn about this mysterious planet. Since the *Phoenix* mission, other spacecraft have been launched to orbit Mars. They have added to the store of new information about our solar system's fourth planet from the sun. Maybe—just maybe—you'll be able to visit Mars yourself someday.

## Summarize

..............................................................................

..............................................................................

..............................................................................

..............................................................................

..............................................................................

# Vocabulary Review

**Word 1    inkling**

**Synonym**

**Word 2    analyze**

**Synonym**

**Word 3    elated**

**Antonym**

**Word 4    monitored**

**Antonym**

| | Active Participation | Interactive Reader | Critical Thinking Application | Week 6 Total |
|---|---|---|---|---|
| **TOTAL POINTS FOR WEEK 6** | | | | |

Follow the Water . . . to Mars!

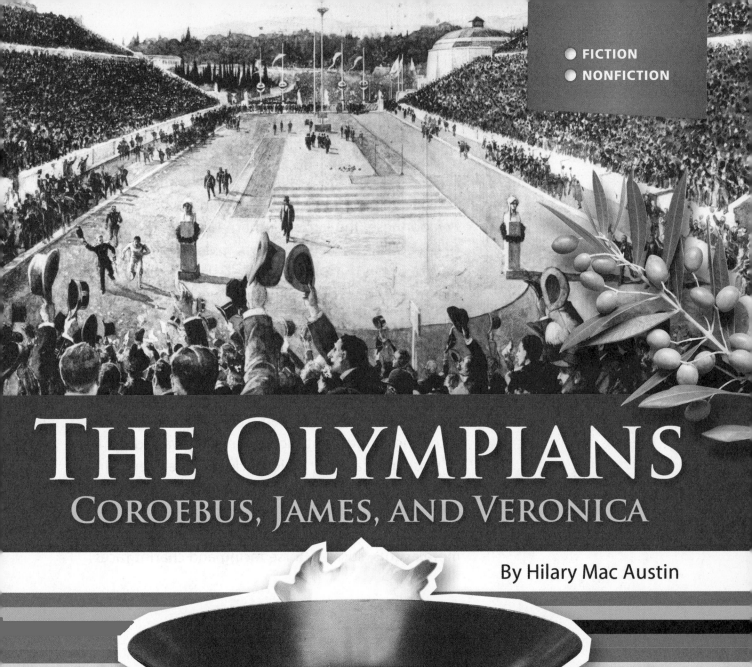

# THE OLYMPIANS
## COROEBUS, JAMES, AND VERONICA

By Hilary Mac Austin

## Build Background

**Word:**

**Definition:**
........................................
........................................
........................................
........................................

**Word:**

**Definition:**
........................................
........................................
........................................
........................................

One hot day late in the summer of 776 B.C., a young man stood sweating and panting at the finish line of a foot race. His name was Coroebus, and he had just won a 210-yard sprint in the first recorded Olympic Games.

These games, part of a festival to honor the god Zeus, were held in Olympia, a city in northwestern Peloponnese, the large southern island in the country of Greece. As a freeborn Greek male, Coroebus could participate in the Olympics. Male slaves and women were not allowed to participate.

The **ancient** Olympics, held every four years, were very different from the Olympics we know today. At the first Olympics there was one event, the foot race won by Coroebus. However as time went on, more types of events were added. There were more foot races and longer foot races. Wrestling was added and so was a pentathlon, which included five events. In addition to a foot race and wrestling, the ancient pentathlon was made up of a long jump, a javelin throw, and a discus throw. Later Olympics added even more events, such as horse racing and chariot races.

## Generate Questions

........................................
........................................
........................................
........................................

The Olympians: Coroebus, James, and Veronica

By 500 B.C., athletic contests were held all over Greece, and the athletes became more professional. As time passed, athletes who competed in the Olympics came from all over the Mediterranean and North Africa. They trained all year and lived on their prize money or on gifts they were given by their proud hometowns. However, the Olympics did not give the athletes money if they won. All the athletes won at the Olympics were **garlands** from the sacred olive groves. Of course, they also won recognition throughout Greece and probably more presents from their hometowns!

In about 100 B.C., Greece was taken over by Rome, and the Olympics became much less important. The competitions were still held, though, until about A.D. 400 when they were abolished.

Almost 2700 years after Coroebus won his race, a young man from the United States stood, panting, at the end of another Olympic event. The young man's name was James Connolly. He had just won the triple jump in the first modern Olympic Games! As many as 60,000 people had watched him win this event.

The Olympians: Coroebus, James, and Veronica

**Word:**
......................................

**Definition:**
......................................

......................................

......................................

**Word:**
......................................

**Definition:**
......................................

......................................

......................................

......................................

James made his famous jump in April 1896, in Athens, Greece. The first modern Olympics were held in that city to honor the ancient games. There were many other connections between the modern and ancient games. Events such as foot races, wrestling, and the discus and javelin throws were held in both the modern and ancient games. **Competitors** were not paid in ancient games and are not paid in the modern games. The modern Olympics happen every four years and so did the ancient games.

However, there are many differences between the ancient Olympics and the modern games. The modern Olympic Games are bigger than the ancient games. In 1896 there were 43 events, and a total of 241 athletes participated. Fourteen countries were represented. There were new events in those first modern games, including fencing, tennis, swimming, and gymnastics. In 1896 the competitors received not only a garland but also a silver medal if they won and a copper medal if they got second place.

Where the Olympics are held is also a big difference between the modern and the ancient games. The modern Olympics are not always held in Greece. The modern games are held in different cities all over the world. Another difference between the modern and the ancient Olympics is the participation of women. In 1896 only men were allowed, as in the ancient games. However, only four years later women began to

## Generate Questions

......................................................................................

......................................................................................

......................................................................................

......................................................................................

......................................................................................

compete. In 1924 another really big change occurred. The Winter Olympics began. Sports in the Winter Olympics include skiing and ice-skating.

Think how much the games have changed since Coroebus ran his race, or even since James Connolly won his event. On August 21, 2008, a woman named Veronica Campbell-Brown stood at the finish line in Beijing, the capital of China. She had just won the gold medal in the 200-meter sprint. Millions of people watched her from their television sets. Veronica was from the small town of Trelawny on the island of Jamaica. She had worked hard all her life to be a runner. She was one of 10,942 athletes from 204 countries at the 2008 Olympics. Her race was one of 302 events. When Veronica stood tall on the **podium** to receive her medal it was not a garland such as Coroebus received. It was not a silver medal such as James received. It was a gold medal for her first place win. At the Olympics today, first place gets gold, second place gets silver, and third place gets bronze.

Despite all of their differences, and despite all the changes over time, Veronica, James, and Coroebus share something. They are linked across the thousands of years and thousands of miles that separate them. They all know what it feels like to be Olympic champions.

Verify Prediction

⭘ CORRECT

⭘ INCORRECT

## Summarize

....................................................................

....................................................................

....................................................................

....................................................................

# Vocabulary Review

**Word 1**

**Definition**

**Word 2**

**Definition**

**Word 3**

**Definition**

**Word 4**

**Definition**

| | Active Participation | Interactive Reader | Critical Thinking Application | Week 7 Total |
|---|---|---|---|---|
| **TOTAL POINTS FOR WEEK 7** | | | | |

The Olympians: Coroebus, James, and Veronica

# Oliver Twist

By Charles Dickens
Retold by Arden Davidson

## Build Background

## Vocabulary

**Word:**

**Definition:**

**Word:**

**Definition:**

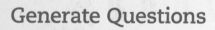

Oliver Twist was not even a day old when he became an orphan. He was born in a workhouse, where poor people in England just barely survived. Oliver's mother, who loved him, didn't live long enough to name him. He got his name from the workhouse board of directors. Oliver cried loudly. If he could have known that he was an orphan, he might have cried louder.

Oliver celebrated his ninth birthday in a basement coal bin, where he'd been sent for punishment. His crime? He was hungry. Oliver and the other little boys labored all day in exchange for a cot and three bowls of thin **gruel.** (An onion twice a week and half a roll on Sunday were special treats.) To put it bluntly, they were starving.

One day, after an especially hard day's work, the boys decided they couldn't take it any longer. So they drew straws to decide which of them would carry out their secret plan. Oliver drew the longest straw, so it was he who had to walk up to the workhouse master, bowl in hand, and say, "Please, sir, I want some more."

## Generate Questions

Oliver Twist

Instead of more food, Oliver got a beating and was sold to the highest bidder. Mr. Sowerberry, a funeral director, offered to buy Oliver as an apprentice (an unpaid helper). It might have been an escape from the workhouse. But Oliver soon learned he had traded one awful place for another.

For months, Oliver quietly endured starvation, beatings, and bullying. But one day Noah, another apprentice, called Oliver's mother names. Suddenly Oliver turned bright red, knocked over the table and chair, and punched Noah so hard he fell over. "His spirit was **roused** at last," Dickens wrote. "The cruel insult to his dead mother had set his blood on fire."

Oliver would not be a victim of abuse any longer. He ran away, with no real plan except to escape and to take care of himself. He ran, hiding behind hedges, afraid he would be followed. And then he saw a stone marker. It said "LONDON 70 MILES." Just the place for a homeless boy! He could earn money, and no one could find him. So with a penny, a crust of bread, a clean shirt, and two pairs of socks, he set off for London.

Oliver Twist

After seven days of walking and sleeping under stairwells, Oliver was weak with hunger. A young boy about his age was staring at him from across the street. Oliver stared back. The boy was dirty, short, and wore a man's coat that reached his feet. They began to talk. Jack Dawkins was his name, "The Artful Dodger" his nickname. Soon he and Oliver were walking the rest of the way to London. Dodger told Oliver that he had a place for him to stay with Fagin, an old man who took care of boys their age. The city was dirty and dark; little children wandered alone. "What an awful place," Oliver thought. But he looked forward to food and rest.

Fagin welcomed Oliver with open arms, and so did the other dozen or so boys that lived with him. However, it wasn't long before Oliver realized there was a catch to living with Fagin. This wasn't just an innocent group of boys; this was a band of pickpockets. They quickly **recruited** Oliver to help them steal men's wallets out of their pockets without being noticed.

Although Fagin pretended to be looking out for Oliver, he was really interested only in the money that the boy could bring in from stealing. Oliver was too innocent to realize this, yet he did not have any trouble figuring out that Bill Sikes, a man who had grown up working for Fagin, was not to be trusted. Sikes was a **hardened** criminal. His girlfriend, Nancy, was a criminal too. But she had a kind heart and really cared for Oliver.

## Generate Questions

Oliver never graduated to actually stealing a wallet. But one day while Dodger and another boy were training him, he got blamed for stealing one. When the man whose money they were stealing turned around, the other two boys ran, and Oliver was just standing there looking guilty.

He tried to run, but he was quickly caught. During the trial, a witness told everyone that Oliver was innocent. The man who had accused him, the kind and wealthy Mr. Brownlow, felt so bad that he decided to let Oliver come and live with him.

The criminals didn't give up. Fagin and Bill Sikes stole Oliver back and tried to use him to commit crimes for them. But Nancy eventually helped him return to the Brownlow Estate, at the cost of her own life: Sikes killed her. Fagin was sentenced to death for his crimes, and Bill Sikes died in an accident

Oliver was finally happy. He had suffered so much that he was able to truly appreciate how lucky he was to be in his new home. Then, to make matters even better, Mr. Brownlow discovered that they were related. Oliver's mother was actually Mr. Brownlow's niece.

Things might not have worked out so well when Oliver first decided to ask for "more." But eventually he got more than he ever dreamed possible.

## Verify Prediction

○ CORRECT

○ INCORRECT

## Summarize

.................................................................

.................................................................

.................................................................

.................................................................

.................................................................

# Vocabulary Review

**Sentence**    I am not fond of eating        every day.

**Sentence**    The alarm        her from her sleep.

**Sentence**    The girls        the new girl for their basketball team.

**Sentence**    The thief was        by years of stealing.

| | Active Participation | Interactive Reader | Critical Thinking Application | Week 8 Total |
|---|---|---|---|---|
| **TOTAL POINTS FOR WEEK 8** | | | | |

# Pure Dead Magic

## Part One

### By Debi Gliori

## Build Background

49

From an upstairs window peered three pairs of eyes. The six eyes watched as a plump woman **negotiated** the moat, apparently unaware of the murderous Tock who dozed in its depths.

"That's the third one this week," observed a voice.

"Fourth, if you count the one that Tock ate for breakfast," said a second voice.

The third pair of eyes blinked. Too young to speak, their owner wondered if *this* one could change diapers and sing the right kind of lullaby to hush a witch baby to sleep.

Having spotted the sleeping crocodile as she crossed the moat, Mrs. McLachlan climbed the steps, sat heavily on a stone griffin guarding the front door, and gazed around. She rooted in a battered handbag and produced a crumpled newspaper advertisement and a pair of reading glasses. Wedging the glasses on the end of her nose, she re-read:

> Energetic nanny/mother's helper urgently required for Titus (12), Pandora (10), and Damp (14 months). The ideal candidate will enjoy a spot of light housework, be well versed in plumbing and veterinary science, have some understanding of cryogenics, and know instinctively how to make French fries that are crunchy on the outside and soft in middle. Hours and salary negotiable.

## Generate Questions

"Take deep breaths, Flora," Mrs. McLachlan commanded herself. "Relax. This is a perfectly ordinary job requiring no magical skills whatsoever. Think nanny. . . ." She refolded the advertisement and tucked it back into her bag. "You want to forget the past?" she continued. "Here is your chance to put it behind you. From the moment you step through this door, you will forget that you were ever a witch."

Above her head, the lintel was decorated with several cherubs peering through an infestation of stone bats. The ugliest of these cherubs had one eye that was not carved in stone but **rendered** in black plastic, and this slid open, rotated slowly, and finally fixed its lens on the woman below.

Upstairs in the observatory, Titus and Pandora examined the new nanny on the closed-circuit television screen. . . .

"Let me see," said Titus.

"I'm looking at her handbag, just now, hang on, I'll move the field a bit."

"Let me *see*," said Titus.

"You're supposed to be watching Damp. I did for ages in the attic, it's your turn. . . . Oh gross!"

"What?"

"She's got hairy legs. . . ."

"Could you stop giving me the picture in the snack-sized bites? LET ME SEE."

"She's nervous, Titus, see for yourself. . . ."

Pure Dead Magic: Part One

Pandora stood up and surrendered her seat to her brother. Titus pressed keys and rolled the mouse with the ease of an expert. The screen in front of him filled with a close-up of the wannabe nanny's face.

"She's so *old,*" he moaned.

"Not as old as that wrinkly on Monday. Remember? The one that called me Panettone and left lipstick kisses all over Damp?"

"Well, she was better than that scary one who went on about the importance of diet for raising children and said that if *she* got the job she'd make sure we ate Brussels sprouts and cabbage every other day."

"Nightmare Nanny," said Pandora. . . .

"Come on, stinkpod," he said, picking up his baby sister and opening the door for Pandora.

"She *hasn't,* has she?" Pandora glared at Damp.

"Oh yes, you have, haven't you, horrible? Phwoarrr . . ." Titus held Damp at arm's length. "Let's go and meet Nanny, shall we?"

"Shall we dress up?" said Pandora. "Flour in the hair? Lipstick blood? Fangs?"

"I suppose so," said Titus, with little enthusiasm. "Rats too?"

"Perfect," Pandora called over her shoulder as she ran downstairs holding her nose. "Although Damp's derriere ought to be quite enough to put any nanny off."

## Generate Questions

Titus followed downstairs, breathing through his mouth. He opened the kitchen door and sighed. Interviewing prospective nannies had been fun at first—introducing them to the pregnant rat Multitundina, meeting Strega-Nonna in her deep freeze, Tock the croc, and all the other scream-inducing creatures that were part of life at StregaSchloss—but after one had watched the nannies turn pale and begin to twitch twenty times or more, the novelty and the glee began to **pall.** Frankly, it was boring. Nannies were boring. Frightening them was boring. And listening to them try to **ingratiate** themselves with the family was MEGA boring.

"Do we *have* to meet her?" Titus said, opening the fridge and gazing at the woeful lack of contents within.

"If we don't," Pandora said in the voice used for explaining large ideas to small people with even smaller IQ's, "Mum might go ahead and hire her, and then we'd end up with someone as horrible as that one who said, 'Much as it pains me to admit, children occasionally need to be spanked soundly for their own good. . . .'"

"I wonder if she tasted as bad as she sounded?" he said.

Pandora hauled Damp out of the compost bucket, scattered a handful of flour over the baby's head, and smiled at her brother. "Only Tock could answer that," she said.

Upstairs the doorbell rang.

## Summarize

# Vocabulary Review

**Word 1**

**Sentence**

**Word 2**

**Sentence**

**Word 3**

**Sentence**

**Word 4**

**Sentence**

| | Active Participation | Interactive Reader | Critical Thinking Application | Week 9 Total |
|---|---|---|---|---|
| **TOTAL POINTS FOR WEEK 9** | | | | |

# Pure Dead Magic

## Part Two

### By Debi Gliori

**Build Background**

**Word:**

**Definition:**

**Word:**

**Definition:**

With a sound that set his teeth on edge, Latch undid bolts, opened padlocks, and turned the vast key in a rusty lock. "You rang?" he said, stating the obvious.

Latch believed in wearing the classic butler's costume of white shirt, black tie, and black jacket. . . .

Scowling horribly, Latch opened the door. On the doorstep stood a woman. She was middle-aged, plump, carried a large handbag of battered plastic, and smelled of lavender.

"Good morning," she said, dragging her gaze upward from Latch's knees to meet his eyes. "I have an appointment with Mrs. Borgia. . . ."

Latch cleared his throat, shuddered slightly, and said, "If modom would be good enough to furnish me with her name?"

"Heavens, laddie, what a **pompous** little person you are. . . . Mrs. McLachlan to youse. Now will you let me in?" And pushing past Latch, Mrs. McLachlan strode into the great hall of StregaSchloss. . . .

"Hold still," commanded Titus.

"I'm trying to," said Pandora, "but Damp wants to hold the lipstick. . . . No! *Damp!* Spit it *out!* Look at her, Titus, she looks like she fell from a great height and used her lips as a break. Oh, Damp, don't dribble. . . ."

"What a disgusting baby," said Titus lovingly. "I think she's perfect for a bit of nanny-baiting, aren't you, Damp?" He stood back to admire the effect.

## Generate Questions

Damp's bottom lip **quivered** ominously.

"And now she's crying . . . told you she'd be perfect," Titus said, turning to grin at his mirrored reflection. . . .

"You look *hideous,*" Pandora said approvingly.

Titus smirked, then hastily readjusted a set of glow-in-the-dark fangs, patted his slicked-down hair and pulled the collar of his cloak tight around his throat. "This ought to do the trick," he said.

"Exit one nanny," Pandora agreed. "Hold Small-and-Smelly till I sort out my veil." She passed the baby over and began to drape her head and shoulders in tattered muslin. Damp made a grab for Titus's fangs.

"Move over, would you?" Pandora nudged her brother. "Stop hogging the mirror."

The three children gazed at their joint reflections. From the mirror, three small vampires gazed back.

"Ready?" Titus wrapped Damp securely in his cloak and opened the kitchen door.

"*Got* you!" Pandora plucked something off the kitchen table and instantly stuffed it down the front of her dress.

"Is that what I think it is?" groaned Titus. "Oh, Pandora, you're so *gross.*"

"Yup," said Pandora, gliding out of the kitchen in a swirl of muslin. "Let's hope the new nanny thinks so too. . . ."

**Word:**

**Definition:**

........................................................

........................................................

........................................................

........................................................

**Word:**

**Definition:**

........................................................

........................................................

........................................................

Signora Strega-Borgia was enchanted. At long last, here was a *normal* person. A person whose day would be full of nursery teas, changing diapers, singing lullabies, and reading stories about happy families of fluffy bunnies. Stories in which Mother Rabbit wasn't a struggling student witch, and Father Rabbit hadn't hopped out of the burrow vowing never to return. . . .

Three weeks ago, her husband, Signor Strega-Borgia, had stormed out of their family home in a temper and since then StregaSchloss had been **shrouded** in a veil of gloom. Despite the fact that their school was shut for the summer, the children rapidly turned mutinous, the staff grew surly, and everyone spoke only in monosyllabic grunts. Dust and cobwebs began to accumulate, giving the whole Schloss an air of neglect. It was as if a fog had descended on the house—everything was colored in shades of gray, and every day was a Monday.

Signora Strega-Borgia choked back a sob and peered hopefully at the woman in front of her. And there, now, in tweeds and sensible shoes, sat an unlikely savior. Here was Nanny McLachlan, who brought with her a blast of bracing Highland air, a gale that might sweep away dust and cobwebs, put a gleam back in the children's eyes, and paint the color back into all their lives. Or at the very least she would be able to rustle up a pan of fries that didn't cause the children to make gagging noises. . . .

## Generate Questions

........................................................................................

........................................................................................

........................................................................................

........................................................................................

........................................................................................

Pure Dead Magic: Part Two

The sound of labored breathing through the keyhole interrupted Signora Strega-Borgia's reverie. "Latch, could you let the children in? I think it's time they met their new nanny."

Latch opened the door with a tug, and Titus, Pandora, and Damp fell into the discouraging room, **thwarted** in their attempts to eavesdrop.

"Get *off* me," roared Pandora, "you're tearing my veil!"

"My fangs are *caught* in your stupid veil, let go of my cloak!"

Squashed under her warring siblings, Damp began to wail.

"Poor wee mite," said a voice, "will she come to me? There, pet, what's this all over your face, och, what a mess you're in."

Mrs. McLachlan scooped Damp onto her lap, cradled her gently against her pillowy chest, and stroked her baby-fluffed head. Damp felt warm and safe. She plugged her lipstick-smeared mouth with a well-sucked thumb, burrowed deeper into that chest, and fell fast asleep.

Blast, thought Latch, she's got the job.

"I've never seen Damp ever do that before," said Signora Strega-Borgia in a reverential voice. "Thank you, Mrs. McLachlan. Now, Titus, Pandora, disentangle yourselves and meet your new nanny. This, my darlings, is Mrs. McLachlan."

Verify Prediction

○ CORRECT

○ INCORRECT

## Summarize

....................................................................................................

....................................................................................................

....................................................................................................

....................................................................................................

....................................................................................................

# Vocabulary Review

**Word 1**

**Definition**

**Word 2**

**Definition**

**Word 3**

**Definition**

**Word 4**

**Definition**

| | Active Participation | Interactive Reader | Critical Thinking Application | Week 10 Total |
|---|---|---|---|---|
| **TOTAL POINTS FOR WEEK 10** | | | | |

Pure Dead Magic: Part Two

- FICTION
- NONFICTION

# WATSON the Supercomputer

By Troy Markham

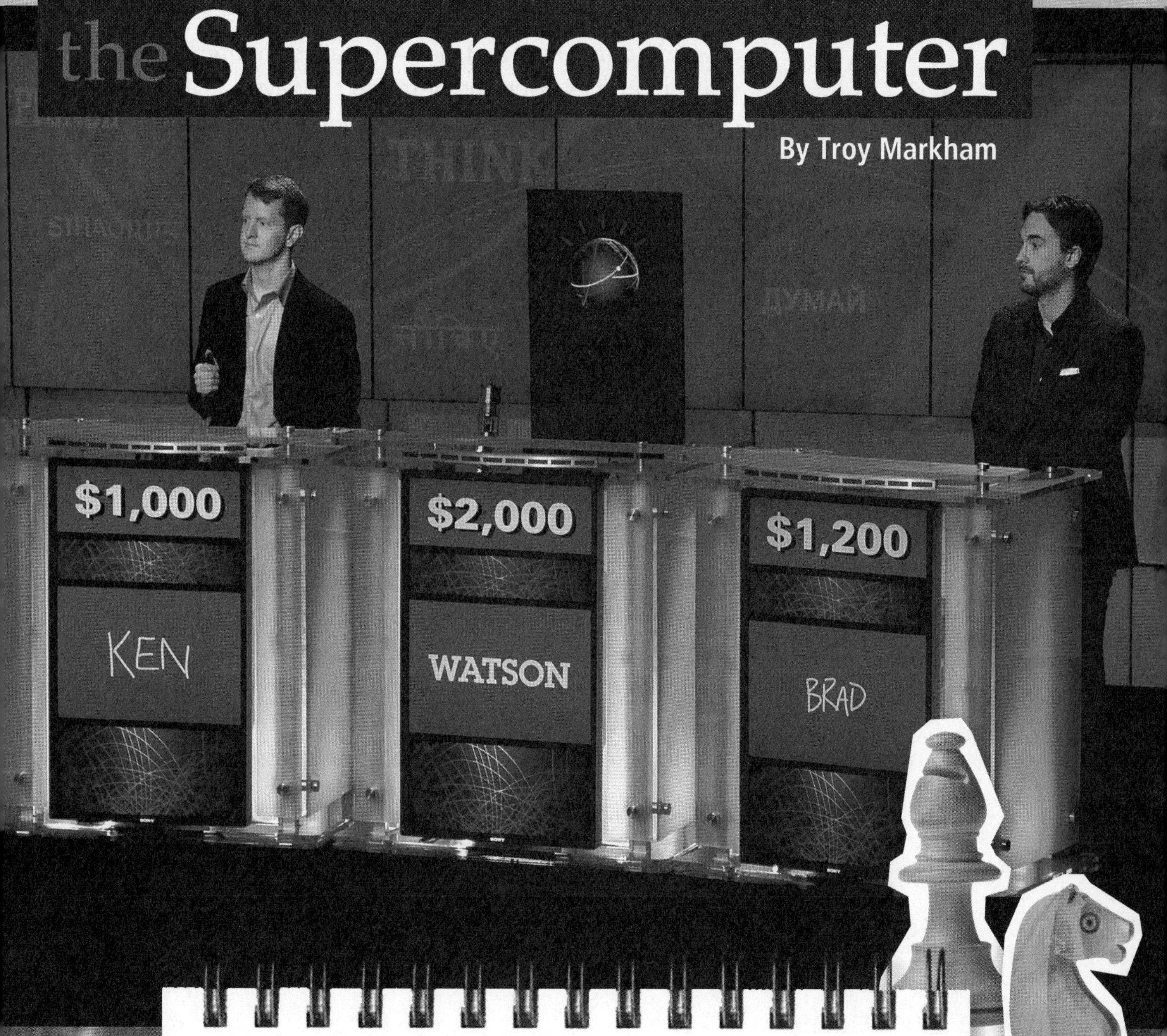

THINK
ДУМАЙ
$1,000
KEN
$2,000
WATSON
$1,200
BRAD

## Build Background

Just about every science-fiction movie features a robot or a computer that acts like a human being. They can be heroes or villains, but they usually share one characteristic—they're smarter than we are.

Could that ever be true? After all, computers are just machines. Even the best don't always do what we tell them to. Are the thinking robots and computers we see in the movies just science fiction?

Computer scientists who work in the field of artificial intelligence—creating machines that copy humans' ability to think—say we may be very close to that reality. And they have backed up their claims by creating better and faster computers with increased abilities. The most recent "intelligent" computer is named Watson. Watson's creation began with a chess-playing ancestor.

IBM computer engineers made a computer named Deep Blue many years ago. It played chess. Although computers can instantly calculate thousands of possible chess moves, a computer had never before beaten a human at chess. This is because chess requires a player to think and **anticipate,** and computers are not capable of these actions. However, Deep Blue was able to finally beat the world's best chess masters.

After Deep Blue's victory, many computer scientists began thinking the same thing: could a computer be designed that would actually take in information, decipher it, and then **reason** to come up with

## Generate Questions

solutions on its own? Such a computer would come very close to the robots and computers in science fiction movies. It was an interesting possibility.

During dinner at a restaurant, one of IBM's research managers noticed that other diners were fixated by the game show *Jeopardy* on the televisions. He wondered if a computer could be designed to play *Jeopardy* against humans. This wasn't an easy problem to work on. It would require a computer that could understand questions asked by a human. It would have to comprehend what was required to answer the questions correctly. And it would have to do it fast. To win *Jeopardy,* contestants not only have to answer correctly, they must also understand the question right away and hit a buzzer first. If the computer could not interpret and determine the solution within seconds, it would not even get the opportunity to answer.

A team of scientists was assigned to the project. At first, things looked bleak. After several months of work, Watson answered *Jeopardy* questions correctly only about fifteen percent of the time. Even worse, the computer was slow, compared to the fast-thinking human contestants. It took several minutes to answer each question. The difficulty was having the computer understand the question and anticipate which answer was expected.

Another complication was *Jeopardy's* format. The computer IBM was developing did not have ears and a brain and a hand to use to buzz in with the answer. The producers of *Jeopardy* were also concerned about Watson's advantages. They worried that the computer might win just because it could activate the buzzer in milliseconds, faster than a human can press a button.

Eventually Watson was hooked up to a mechanism that had to be physically activated by the computer. Although Watson was still faster, the humans were better at anticipating the questions.

Finally, after two years, the programmers had a system that could compete on *Jeopardy.* Watson would compete against Ken Jennings and Brad Rutter, two of the most successful past *Jeopardy* champions. Both men were excited to take on Watson, and *Jeopardy* viewers were **eager** to watch the competition.

Many people believe that Watson transmitted questions onto the Internet in order to find answers, but this was not the case. Watson was programmed with libraries of stored information. Whenever questions were presented, Watson analyzed clue words in the question. It then attempted to match the clues to the stored information. Like Jennings and Rutter, sometimes Watson could not decide which information was correct. For each question, the computer calculated a percentage that its answer was right. This percentage was a confidence level. If the confidence level was high enough, Watson buzzed in to answer.

## Generate Questions

The match went two rounds. Although Watson dominated both rounds, the contest showed that humans have advantages. Jeopardy questions are in categories, and sometimes the category name is funny, misleading, or unclear. Watson didn't know how to tell the difference. So when one question in the category "U.S. Cities" asked for a city with an airport named after a World War II hero and battle, Watson was confused. It answered "Toronto." Wrong! Toronto is in Canada. Rutter and Jennings correctly answered "Chicago." Another question asked about an oddity. Watson couldn't answer because it didn't know what made something odd.

The final tally was $77,147 for Watson, $24,000 for Jennings, and $21,600 for Rutter. Watson had soundly defeated the humans. And once more, the science-fiction **scenario** of intelligent computers crept closer to reality.

But Ken Jennings thinks there's hope. "Watson might be able to answer a clue, but it could never write a new one," Jennings told a reporter. "It can figure out how to tell a joke, but it will never laugh at it."

Verify Prediction

◯ CORRECT

◯ INCORRECT

Summarize

.........................................................................................................................

.........................................................................................................................

.........................................................................................................................

.........................................................................................................................

.........................................................................................................................

# Vocabulary Review

**Sentence** You need to read the math problem carefully and then through it before answering.

**Sentence** The the teacher described helped her see a bright future.

**Sentence** I was to see what was in the package.

**Sentence** I tried to what her next move would be.

| | Active Participation | Interactive Reader | Critical Thinking Application | Week 11 Total |
|---|---|---|---|---|
| **TOTAL POINTS FOR WEEK 11** | | | | |

# GUINNESS
## WORLD RECORDS

By Hilary Mac Austin

## Build Background

**Word:**
...............................................

**Definition:**
...............................................

...............................................

...............................................

...............................................

**Word:**
...............................................

**Definition:**
...............................................

...............................................

...............................................

...............................................

...............................................

"Golden plovers are the fastest game bird in Britain," a hunter remarks as he watches the birds fly into the sky.

"Not so," replies his friend. "The fastest game bird is the grouse."

"My good man," says the first man, getting a bit red in the face, "I hate to disagree, but it is the plover. I'm absolutely certain of it."

"No, my dear fellow. I'm afraid you are mistaken. I know my birds, and I know it's the grouse."

"Hrmph! Know your birds. As if I don't know mine. Hrmph! Been hunting 'em since I was a lad. It's the plover!" says the first man, now becoming quite **agitated.**

"Grouse!" growls the second man.

"Plover, I say," seethes the first man.

Have you ever had an argument like this? Have you ever thought you knew a fact, but a friend said you were wrong? Did that make you mad? When you get into an argument about a fact, do you Google the answer? How in the world did people settle such arguments before the Internet was invented? They looked in *The Guinness Book of World Records.*

In 1951 Sir Hugh Beaver was hunting birds with friends at Castlebridge House in County Wexford, Ireland. The group wanted to know the fastest game

## Generate Questions

...............................................................................

...............................................................................

...............................................................................

...............................................................................

bird in Europe. (A game bird is a wild bird that is hunted for sport and food. Pheasants, grouse, quail, and plovers are game birds.) Castlebridge House had a large reference library, but to the men's frustration the answer couldn't be found in any book in it.

This gave Hugh Beaver an idea. He realized that there must be unsettled arguments all over England and Ireland, especially in pubs where people gathered to drink, visit, and talk. He thought it would be a smart idea to have a book of facts and records in all of these pubs. Beaver knew a lot about pubs. He was not just any rich man. He was the managing director of the Guinness Brewery, which made the most famous beer in Ireland.

For three years Beaver thought about his idea. Then he met Norris and Ross McWhirter, twins who ran the McWhirter Fact and Figure Agency in London. He hired them right away. The McWhirter twins immediately gathered a staff and set to work. They sent letters to all kinds of scientists. They also came up with an unusual way to get the answers they needed. They didn't ask experts to give them the facts. They asked the experts to *correct* facts they had thought up themselves. According to the twins, "We found that people who have a total resistance to giving information often have an irresistible desire to correct other people's **impressions.**"

**Word:**

**Definition:**

...........................................................

...........................................................

...........................................................

...........................................................

**Word:**

**Definition:**

...........................................................

...........................................................

...........................................................

...........................................................

After working around the clock for thirteen weeks, the twins got the book to the printers. No one was prepared for how popular it would be. Everyone seemed to want to know about records and amazing **feats.** By Christmas 1955, *The Guinness Book of Records* was the best-selling book in England.

Surprisingly, the question about the fastest bird wasn't answered in the first *Guinness Book.* In fact, it wasn't answered until 1989. According to the book, the red grouse is the fastest. It can fly up to sixty-three miles per hour for short periods.

Every year a new edition of the book with updated information is **published.** Over the years, the book's title has changed, first to *The Guinness Book of World Records,* then to *Guinness World Records.* In 2001 the company split from the Guinness Brewery. Today there are *Guinness World Records* video games, a website, and television shows in addition to the book.

## Generate Questions

...........................................................................................................................

...........................................................................................................................

...........................................................................................................................

...........................................................................................................................

...........................................................................................................................

*Guinness World Records* still keeps track of the tallest person on earth (Sultan Kosen of Turkey, who is eight feet three inches tall) and the shortest man (Khagendra Thapa Magar of Nepal, who is 26.4 inches tall and weighs thirteen pounds). It still records amazing feats of human endurance and achievement. For example, on April 1, 2010, Stig Åvall Severinsen of Denmark became the new record holder for holding his breath underwater. He did it for twenty minutes and ten seconds!

However, more and more, Guinness records the amazing and the strange. The person with the longest fingernails was Melvin Boothe of Troy, Michigan, whose combined fingernail length was 32 feet 3.8 inches. The fastest skateboard speed from a standing position is 70.21 miles per hour. This record was achieved by Douglas da Silva of Brazil on October 20, 2007.

How many straws can fit in a human mouth? Four hundred. What is the longest hair measured on a human? Eighteen feet 5.54 inches. What is the largest gathering of Santa Clauses on earth? Thirteen thousand. These are only a few of the thousands of strange and amazing feats recorded by *Guinness World Records.* Anyone can apply to set a record. How about you?

## Verify Prediction

○ CORRECT

○ INCORRECT

## Summarize

......................................................................

......................................................................

......................................................................

......................................................................

......................................................................

# Vocabulary Review

**Word 1** published

**Synonym**

**Word 2** impressions

**Synonym**

**Word 3** agitated

**Antonym**

**Word 4** feats

**Antonym**

| TOTAL POINTS FOR WEEK 12 | Active Participation | Interactive Reader | Critical Thinking Application | Week 12 Total |
|---|---|---|---|---|
| | | | | |

# Henrietta Lacks

## *A Life That Keeps Giving Life*

By Kathleen Thompson
and Leah Pietrusiak

## Build Background

Henrietta Lacks never went to medical school. She wasn't a doctor, a nurse, or a scientist. And yet she is one of the most important women in medical history.

Lacks, who was African American, was born in 1920. She grew up planting and harvesting tobacco plants in Virginia. Lacks moved to a city in nearby Maryland after she married, but she worked on the farm every weekend. She liked to help other people. When family members or friends needed help, she let them stay at her house and cooked for them, even though she was poor herself. They loved her rice pudding.

Lacks also took care of a cousin who had polio, a **contagious** disease that can paralyze and even kill people. She wished she could help him. Little did Lacks know that she was going to help many others in the fight against polio . . . and many other diseases.

## Generate Questions

Henrietta Lacks: A Life That Keeps Giving Life

Lacks and her husband, David, had five children. Shortly after her last baby was born, Lacks started having a bad pain in her abdomen. When she touched where it hurt, it felt like a big knot. The pain was so severe she went to a doctor.

Dr. Howard Jones discovered the knot was a **tumor.** Unfortunately the tumor was cancerous. But something else caught his attention. Lacks had been treated at the hospital three months before, and there was no sign of a tumor. The doctor couldn't understand how it had grown to be so big so fast.

In the human body, cells divide all the time to heal wounds or to grow hair or muscle. This cell division is called mitosis. But if something goes wrong, the cells can start growing out of control. That's what cancer is.

Lacks's cells were multiplying much faster than the cells of other cancer patients. The doctor was interested in this because, at that time, scientists needed cancer cells to do research, but they could not keep human cells alive for very long outside the body. For example, they wanted to test medicines to see whether they killed cancer cells. Because Lacks's cells were multiplying so fast, her doctor thought they might not die outside her body and could be used for research.

Make Prediction

Henrietta Lacks went back to Johns Hopkins Hospital in Baltimore, Maryland, for surgery. The surgeon took another sample of her cells. He sent them to George Gey (pronounced *guy*), a research scientist. Gey and his wife, Margaret Gey, were working to find a cure for cancer. They had been trying to grow cancer cells in a laboratory, but the cells died quickly, and they certainly didn't grow.

When Lacks's cells arrived, a laboratory assistant put her cells into different test tubes. She wrote "HeLa" (pronounced *hee-luh*) on each tube in big black letters. "HeLa" referred to the first two letters of Lacks's first name and the first two letters of her last name. Then the Geys waited to see whether Lacks's cells died like the others.

They didn't. In fact, they doubled! And they kept growing.

Henrietta Lacks gave scientists the world's first **immortal** cells. They became known as "HeLa cells." George Gey sent HeLa cells to scientists around the world so they could use them for cancer research.

Lacks died in 1951, eight months after the doctor found her tumor, but her cells lived on and continued to multiply. Shortly after Lacks's death, HeLa cells were used to test a vaccine for polio, the terrible disease Lacks's cousin had. Scientists needed a huge number of cells to test the vaccine. Using HeLa cells, they made a vaccine that worked. Polio is now almost wiped out.

## Generate Questions

Henrietta Lacks: A Life That Keeps Giving Life

There's no way of knowing how many trillions of HeLa cells are used in laboratories today. But if you laid all the HeLa cells ever created next to each other, they would wrap around the world at least three times. And one cell is about the size of a period on this page!

In the years since Lacks's death, HeLa cells have been used to create important cancer medicines. They've been used to learn more about how to treat blindness. They've been **crucial** in learning about diseases like AIDS. HeLa cells have even been sent into space to see how human cells change at zero gravity.

Lacks's cells have become famous for another reason. The HeLa cells were used without Lacks's permission. Although that's illegal today, it was common in the 1950s, especially when the patient was African American. Lacks's husband, children, and grandchildren had no idea the HeLa cells were hers until the 1970s.

However, thanks to Lacks and her HeLa cells, scientists have been able to do research that keeps people alive. Henrietta Lacks helped people during her life and continues to help people even after her death.

## Verify Prediction

◯ CORRECT

◯ INCORRECT

## Summarize

**Word 1**

**Definition**

**Word 2**

**Definition**

**Word 3**

**Definition**

**Word 4**

**Definition**

| TOTAL POINTS FOR WEEK 13 | Active Participation | Interactive Reader | Critical Thinking Application | Week 13 Total |
|---|---|---|---|---|
| | | | | |

# BREAD:
## All You "Knead" to Know

By Arden Davidson

## Build Background

**Word:**

**Definition:**

**Word:**

**Definition:**

**Chances are** that no matter where you live in America, you've probably eaten a tortilla. Maybe it was a wrap for lunch, rolled around meat, cheese, or vegetables. How about a pita, the round, flat bread with a handy pocket inside for all your sandwich fixings?

It might surprise you that people have been eating this kind of bread, called flatbread, for about ten thousand years. The first flatbread would have been made by pounding grains of wheat into flour, mixing the flour with a bit of water to make dough, and tossing it onto a hot rock next to a fire to bake.

Flatbreads haven't changed much since then. They're found in almost every culture, from South Asia to as far north as Norway and Sweden. In every place they're a little different. In the Mediterranean and the Mideast, pitas are used to scoop dips such as hummus or as a wrap to make a sandwich of kebab (pieces of meat sometimes cooked on metal rods called skewers) or even salad. In India, Pakistan, and Afghanistan, flatbread is called *naan*. Naan is baked in a clay oven called a tandoor. Tortillas originated in Mexico, first made by the Aztecs from corn about the same time the Egyptians began making bread. *Tortilla* means "little cake" in Spanish; tortillas are used to make burritos, enchiladas, and many other tasty dishes, usually with meat.

## Generate Questions

Bread: All You "Knead" to Know

Bread is basic. It's called "the staff of life"—a necessary food. In many parts of the world, it's about the only thing poor people had to eat. The ingredients are simple: grain, such as wheat, corn, or barley; water or other liquid; salt; and usually yeast. Yeast occurs naturally when grain ferments, or gives off carbon dioxide. That's what makes bread rise. Yeast also gives bread a light, chewy texture and a great taste.

Perhaps it's obvious, but all bread has a fifth ingredient: heat. It needs to be baked. Egyptians made the earliest portable ovens from clay, shaped like a beehive. In the bottom half was the fire, made from sticks, dry grass, or animal droppings. The bread was baked in the top half. The early Jews hollowed out stone to make their ovens. In Jerusalem there was a bakers' quarter where bread was baked in **tiers** inside tall ovens. The ovens were called "furnaces" in the Bible. Often ovens were inside in the main room of the house. People hollowed out a place in the floor, covered it with clay, and laid a fire. When the embers had burned down, they were scooped out and the bread dough placed in the hollow to bake.

Make Prediction

In the Middle Ages, the type of bread you ate was a clue to your social status. The rich could afford white bread made with soft wheat flour. Peasants ate dark bread made with millet, barley, or rye. The bakers of London were divided into two groups: brown and white. The authorities wanted to make sure that brown bread contained the whole grain so that the poor would get good **nutrition.** That was important when your diet consisted mostly of bread.

Bakers, as you might imagine, were important people. Ovens were improved and made big enough to bake many loaves at a time. At first, women would bring their families' dough to the village baker to bake in his oven. Bakers eventually became responsible for providing all the bread for the community, for a price. The average 18th century worker spent half his daily wage on bread. When poor crops and government policy forced up the price of bread in France in the 1700s, the peasants rioted. The gap between rich and poor fueled their anger and became an issue in the French Revolution.

Bread making changed with modern advances in cooking and preserving. Louis Pasteur made a discovery in 1859 that allowed yeast to be sold commercially (for money). This allowed bread to be mass-produced more cheaply and efficiently than ever before.

## Generate Questions

Bread: All You "Knead" to Know

In the 1920s and 30s, companies began making bread with refined flour. White bread was very popular. It was softer and stayed fresh longer than whole grain bread, but it turned out to be less nutritious. It's **ironic** that brown bread, which in the Middle Ages marked a person as poor, is often more expensive now. Less nutritious white bread is more readily available at lower prices, while more nutritious whole-grain bread tends to be more expensive.

The different varieties of bread are endless. There are bagels, cinnamon rolls, breadsticks, long crusty French baguettes, Italian bread made with garlic and herbs, British scones, American cornbread, Russian dark rye, and the flatbreads from all over the world. It's hard to believe that they all started from a simple Egyptian mixture of wheat, water, and heat. So next time you're eating pizza, gyros, tacos, or a slice of French bread, say a little silent "thank you" to whoever those first bread makers were. They deserve it.

Verify Prediction

○ CORRECT

○ INCORRECT

## Summarize

........................................................................................................

........................................................................................................

........................................................................................................

........................................................................................................

........................................................................................................

# Vocabulary Review

**Sentence** It's _____ that on the day I wore my heavy coat it got really warm outside.

**Sentence** _____ you will pass the test if you study.

**Sentence** If you want to be healthy, you should exercise and try to get good _____ .

**Sentence** The wedding cake had four _____ , each one smaller than the one below it.

| | Active Participation | Interactive Reader | Critical Thinking Application | Week 14 Total |
|---|---|---|---|---|
| TOTAL POINTS FOR WEEK 14 | | | | |

Bread: All You "Knead" to Know

# SOLDIER'S HEART

## Part One

### By Gary Paulsen

## Build Background

**Word:**

**Definition:**

**Word:**

**Definition:**

### Foreword

War is always, in all ways, **appalling.** Lives are stopped in youth, worlds are ended, and even for those who survive—and the vast majority of soldiers who go to war *do* survive—the mental damage done is often permanent.

Now there is an attempt to understand this form of injury and deal with it. It is called post-traumatic stress disorder by those who try to cure it.

But in other times and other wars, they used more descriptive terms.

In the Second World War the mental damage was called battle fatigue, and there were **rudimentary** efforts to help the victims. These usually involved bed rest and the use of sedatives or other drugs.

## Generate Questions

In the First World War it was called shell shock, based on the damage done by the overwhelming use, for the first time in modern war, of artillery fire against soldiers in stationary positions (trenches). The concussion of exploding incoming rounds, thousands upon thousands of them, often left men deaf and dazed, many of them with a symptom called the thousand-yard stare. The afflicted were essentially not helped at all and simply sent home for their families to care for. Most were irrational; many were in a vegetative state.

In the Civil War the syndrome was generally not recognized at all. While the same horrors existed as those in modern war, in some ways they were even worse because the technological aspect of war being born then, the wholesale killing by men using raw firepower, was so new and misunderstood. The same young men were fed into madness. But in those days there was no scientific knowledge of mental disorders and no effort was made to help the men who were damaged. Some men came through combat unscathed. Most did not. These men were somehow different from other men.

They were said to have soldier's heart.

**Word:**
.................................................
**Definition:**
.................................................
.................................................
.................................................
.................................................

**Word:**
.................................................
**Definition:**
.................................................
.................................................
.................................................
.................................................

**June 1861**

There was going to be a shooting war. They were having town meetings and nailing up posters all over Minnesota and the excitement was so high Charley had seen girls faint at the meetings, just faint from the noise and hullabaloo. It was better than a circus. Or what he thought a circus must be like. He'd never seen anything but Winona, Minnesota, and the river five miles each way from town.

There would be a shooting war. There were rebels who had **violated** the law and fired on Fort Sumter and the only thing they'd respect was steel, it was said, and he knew they were right, and the Union was right, and one other thing they said as well—if a man didn't hurry he'd miss it. The only shooting war to come in a man's life and if a man didn't step right along he'd miss the whole thing.

Charley didn't figure to miss it. The only problem was that Charley wasn't rightly a man yet, at least not to the army. He was fifteen and while he worked as a man worked, in the fields all of a day and into night, and looked like a man standing tall and just a bit thin with hands so big they covered a stove lid, he didn't make a beard yet and his voice had only just dropped enough so he could talk with men.

If they knew, he thought, if they knew he was but fifteen they wouldn't take him at all.

## Generate Questions

.................................................
.................................................
.................................................
.................................................
.................................................
.................................................

But Charley watched and Charley listened and Charley learned.

Minnesota was forming a volunteer regiment to go off and fight. It would have near on a thousand men when it was full, men from Winona and Taylor's Falls and Mankato and as far north as Deerwood and from the capital, St. Paul, as well.

A thousand men. And Charley had learned one thing about an army: One part of an army didn't always know the business of another part. The thousand men in the **regiment** would be in companies of eighty to a hundred men from each section and it would be hard for a man to know men who weren't from the same area.

Charley couldn't join where they knew him. Somebody would spill the beans and he'd get sent back or used as a runner or drummer boy. He wasn't any boy. He was going to sign to fight as a man and he knew a way to do it.

They would gather at Fort Snelling, up along the Mississippi. All the companies from all the towns would assemble there before they went off to fight.

He'd just take him a walk, Charley would, take a walk by himself until he was at Fort Snelling and there he would lie about his age and sign up as a man and get him a musket and a uniform and go to see what a war was like.

Verify Prediction

◯ CORRECT

◯ INCORRECT

## Summarize

........................................................................

........................................................................

........................................................................

........................................................................

........................................................................

# Vocabulary Review

### Word 1

**Sentence**

### Word 2

**Sentence**

### Word 3

**Sentence**

### Word 4

**Sentence**

| | Active Participation | Interactive Reader | Critical Thinking Application | Week 15 Total |
|---|---|---|---|---|
| TOTAL POINTS FOR WEEK 15 | | | | |

# SOLDIER'S HEART

## Part Two

### By Gary Paulsen

## Build Background

**Word:** ............................................

**Definition:** ....................................

............................................................

............................................................

............................................................

**Word:** ............................................

**Definition:** ....................................

............................................................

............................................................

............................................................

"I won't get into any trouble, Ma," he said, wrapping some bread and cold potatoes and half a roast chicken in some tow cotton. "Plus they'll be paying me. I hear they give eleven dollars a month. I'll send most of it on home to you and Orren." Orren was his younger brother. "You can use the money and I won't be under your feet all the time. . . ."

"You aren't under my feet." She hated it when he talked fast. He always got his way when he talked fast. He'd smile and that **cowlick** would stand up in the back and he'd talk fast and she couldn't keep him from what he wanted. He was a good boy, as good as they came, but ever since his father, Paul, had been kicked to death by a horse gone mad when a swarm of bees landed on it, Charley only had to smile and talk fast and he got his way. "You haven't ever been under my feet."

"Same as," he said, shaking his head. "I'm always in the way. Best I go off and see what the big fuss is all about."

"You ain't but a boy."

## Generate Questions

....................................................................................................

....................................................................................................

....................................................................................................

....................................................................................................

"And I've got to be a man sometime. You've said it more than once yourself. Charley, you said, you've got to be a man. Well, here it is—my chance to be a man. A boy wouldn't go off to earn eleven dollars a month and wear a uniform. Only a man. So I'm going to be a man and do what a man can do."

And he won. She knew he would and he did and he took his bread and cold potatoes and chicken and left home walking down the road for Fort Snelling, and if she had known what was to come of it, she would have fought to drag him back and let the federal government keep their eleven dollars a month.

But she also had heard the songs and the **slogans** and seen the parades, had been to the meetings and though it was her son Charley leaving she did not think it would be so bad. Nobody thought it would be so bad. Nobody thought it *could* be so bad. And all the officers and politicians and newspapers said it would be a month or two, no longer.

It would all be over by fall.

## Fort Snelling

They didn't have uniforms for him. There was a pair of black pants that were so short his calves showed, a pair of gray socks, and a black felt hat. That was the uniform he received to go for a soldier.

They took his name. The colonel of the regiment read a list of things he couldn't do—desert his post, traffic with the enemy, steal from his fellow soldiers, act immoral or without decency—and then he signed his name, told them he was eighteen and they didn't challenge it, and he was a soldier.

There wasn't much of a war, Charley decided early on, but there was a lot of playacting and once he got inside it he found it mostly boring.

They did something they called "drills" and the "manual of arms," working in the hot sun in the compound area of Fort Snelling until they were soaked with sweat and Charley felt he could snap his rifle from left shoulder heft to right shoulder heft as good as any man in any army had ever done it.

They fired some but there wasn't much ammunition and when the sergeants tried to make them hit targets a quarter mile off, Charley nearly laughed.

## Generate Questions

But they practiced anyway and stood and fired and dropped to one knee, and then the next rank stood and fired and dropped. They reloaded by biting the end off the paper cartridge, pouring the powder down the bore and setting the bullet on the powder with the ramrod.

When they couldn't afford to **expend** any more live ammunition they practiced with empty rifles, again and again, until Charley was sick to death of the drilling and wheeling and marching and fake loading.

It would be different, he thought, if the leaders knew what they were doing. But the officers and sergeants had been civilians like the rest of the men and mostly had been elected by the men themselves and had to learn as they went along, using an army manual for close-order drill.

It seemed all they did was drill and sweat and listen to sergeants and corporals **bellow** at them and as the weeks passed Charley grew more and more bored and was beginning to pay attention to his mother's letters. She had taken to thinking of the bad side of the war and was in fear that Charley would get killed and wrote three times a week.

"I know it ain't right," she wrote in one letter, "but you must think on coming home now. Just leave the army and walk home before they get you in a battle and shoot you apart. . . ."

## Verify Prediction

◯ CORRECT

◯ INCORRECT

## Summarize

...........................................................................................................

...........................................................................................................

...........................................................................................................

...........................................................................................................

# Vocabulary Review

**Word 1**

**Definition**

**Word 2**

**Definition**

**Word 3**

**Definition**

**Word 4**

**Definition**

| | Active Participation | Interactive Reader | Critical Thinking Application | Week 16 Total |
|---|---|---|---|---|
| **TOTAL POINTS FOR WEEK 16** | | | | |

● FICTION
● NONFICTION

# SOLDIER'S HEART

## Part Three

By Gary Paulsen

### Build Background

## Fort Snelling

Like most of the men, Charley doubted there ever would be a battle. Minnesota was mostly wild then, with Sioux and Chippewa Indians to the north and west, and there were some **frontier** forts on the edge of the wilderness to deal with any difficulties. These posts were manned by regular army troops, which Lincoln needed now to fight in the war, and there was talk in the ranks that the Minnesota volunteers would be used to replace the army troops at the frontier forts so the regular army could go east to fight.

"It'll be all mosquitoes and muck," a corporal named Massey said during a break in drilling one afternoon. "They don't let me go fight the rebels and I might pull foot and leave. . . ."

It was all rumor, of course, but what with his mother's letters (she wrote more often all the time of deserting), the boredom of constant drilling in the hot sun, and now the talk of being sent to relieve the frontier forts so that the regular army troops could go fight the Rebels (one company had already been started on the march north to the forts), Charley was nearly on the edge of leaving when on June 22 they were called into formation, ordered to get all their gear and marched to the river, where steamboats were waiting to take them to St. Paul.

## Generate Questions

There they marched through town with great **fanfare.** They still didn't have proper uniforms but they had all been issued red flannel shirts, and though those shirts were as hot as original sin—as Charley heard them described—at least the men looked like a unit, marching with shouldered rifles and hats cocked forward. Girls waved flags and people yelled, "Go it, boys, get the Rebels!" and "Don't stop till you hit Richmond!"

In a short time they boarded other steamboats that took them south and east to La Crosse, Wisconsin, where trains were waiting for them.

It was all new to him. Charley had never ridden on a steamboat, never marched in a parade or had pretty girls wave flags for him and hand him sweets. Now, as he boarded the train and saw the plush seats and fancy inside of the car, he thought: I never, I just never imagined such a thing existed.

It was, all in all, a simply grand way to go off to fight a war.

Soldier's Heart: Part Three

**Word:**
.................................................

**Definition:**
.................................................

.................................................

.................................................

.................................................

.................................................

**Word:**
.................................................

**Definition:**
.................................................

.................................................

.................................................

.................................................

### Toward Manassas

He thought he would remember the train ride forever. Most of the men had never been on a train and certainly few of them had been on one this **plush.** The seats were soft and cushiony and the food—especially compared to the rough **fare** at Fort Snelling—was delicious.

They rode across Wisconsin and down into Chicago and everywhere they stopped there were huge crowds gathered to cheer them on. Girls gave them hankies and sweets and Charley figured later he had fallen in love at least a dozen times.

The country didn't change much at first and it was still all Union. They made their way—sleeping like lords and eating like kings, Charley thought—across Illinois, Indiana, Ohio, Pennsylvania and down into Maryland, and there were crowds all the way, even when the train didn't stop.

Charley saw his first coloreds when they moved into Maryland. They looked poor and had poor clothes and he thought about slavery then and how it must be strange to own a person so they had to do what you wanted.

## Generate Questions

.................................................

.................................................

.................................................

.................................................

.................................................

Soldier's Heart: Part Three

A woman of color came up to him when the train was stopped in Maryland, just before Baltimore, and handed him a sweet roll and said, "Thank you for what you're doing. I hope God keeps you safe from harm and brings you back to your family."

Now the country was changing. There had been farms all along, and towns, but the trees seemed more spaced here, the pastures more open, and Charley began to see "poor" farms. He'd heard the men talking about them, the poor whites, but he still wasn't quite ready for the sight when the train slowed for a hill and passed a shack that was little more than boards tacked to some poles.

He stared out the window and thought of all the things he would tell his mother and his brother, Orren, when he wrote the next letter.

*I'm a man now,* he would write, *and seeing and doing a man's things out in the world. I've seen things you wouldn't believe. . . .*

He leaned back, closed his eyes and let the gentle rocking of the train take him to sleep.

## Summarize

......................................................................................................................

......................................................................................................................

......................................................................................................................

......................................................................................................................

# Vocabulary Review

**Sentence**   The ___ was spicy and hot.

**Sentence**   The hero deserves a lot of ___ and recognition.

**Sentence**   The ___ chairs at the hotel looked really comfortable.

**Sentence**   The pioneers moved to the ___ in order to buy new land.

| | Active Participation | Interactive Reader | Critical Thinking Application | Week 17 Total |
|---|---|---|---|---|
| **TOTAL POINTS FOR WEEK 17** | | | | |

# KEEPING CLEAN IN THE MIDDLE AGES: POSITIVELY MEDIEVAL

### By Troy Markham

## Build Background

In the late 1500s, Queen Elizabeth I of England took one bath every month. The peasants and townspeople might have grumbled to themselves. One bath every month? That was just **ludicrous.** No one needed to bathe that often—and if you could, it meant you were beyond wealthy and could afford such luxuries. Queen Elizabeth, in her castle surrounded by servants and anything she needed, seemed to agree with them. She told the people she bathed every month "whether I need it or not."

In the castle and villages at that time, hot water was hard to come by. To prepare her bath, for example, Elizabeth required a troop of servants. Large quantities of water had to be drawn. Then fires had to be stoked and maintained to heat the water. Finally her army of helpers had to hoist the water in buckets up long flights of stairs to her bathing chambers. It was quite an ordeal.

Among the peasants, there was a casual attitude about keeping clean. There were no bathrooms. People generally used the bathroom in buckets or chamber pots. How did they dispose of the waste? For the most part they just threw the contents out the window onto the streets! Even the nobles, such as Elizabeth, did not have running water or sewage systems. There was no garbage collection, so trash was thrown anywhere and left to rot.

## Generate Questions

Keeping Clean in the Middle Ages: Positively Medieval

To be fair, one of the reasons that people at the time were unconcerned about cleanliness and hygiene was because they did not understand the **consequences.** Even the scientists of the time did not make the connection between disease and sickness and sanitary conditions. Often food, dirt, and other waste were left to layer the surfaces of houses where edibles would sit. Cooks and servants did not bother to wash their hands when preparing or handling meals.

It was also not out of disregard that people avoided bathing. The huge expense of time and currency made it impossible for common people to have baths. Bathing, such as Elizabeth enjoyed monthly, was seen as a luxury. The public had to get by with washing infrequently in rivers and lakes or occasionally at home, most often with cold water. Early soaps and cleaning resources were made from a variety of sources. Most soaps of the time were constructed from animal fat, ash, lye, clay, or other similar materials. The trouble of preparing a bath meant that typically several people would share the same water, or even bathe together. There were public baths (bath houses), typically near the river, where it was easy to get water. Groups of people bathed together, and these places were called "stews."

Oddly enough, though, some royalty found bathing and cleaning important enough to spend a considerable fortune on. In the early 1400s, well before Elizabeth was taking her monthly bath in the 1500s, the Duke of Burgundy, John the Fearless, was building a bathroom.

The duke had constructed within his palace the first "water closet," a specific room to serve as a bathroom. Generally, even royalty simply did their business behind screens or in corners or out-of-the-way areas within their bedrooms. John's bathroom contained a structure that still exists and looks remarkably like the toilets we use today. It featured a padded seat and a ventilation system designed to keep the room from becoming smelly. In addition, the room was heated for comfort by a nearby chimney. Remarkably, the toilet even had a removal system composed of a long pipe that led through the floor and into a closed pit outside the palace. The pit had a slotted floor to allow liquid to filter away. The Duke had the pit emptied periodically and kept it sealed to prevent odors from escaping. It was an amazing **innovation** for its day.

## Generate Questions

Keeping Clean in the Middle Ages: Positively Medieval

Queen Elizabeth I had no such water closet. Her monthly bathing ritual, however, displayed her regard for hygiene and cleanliness. This view may have been influenced by the experience of the Black Plague a century or two before, which killed millions. As scientists began to realize that poor hygiene was **detrimental** to health, more of an effort was made to wash regularly.

And so, every thirty days throughout Elizabeth's reign as queen, the servants did her bidding to maintain her hygiene. They heated buckets and buckets of water over hot fires. They lifted the heavy buckets up long flights of stairs to the queen's chamber. And they kept those fires going, the water heating, and the buckets climbing. For a queen's bath must never be allowed to cool.

## Verify Prediction

○ CORRECT

○ INCORRECT

## Summarize

..........................................................................................................

..........................................................................................................

..........................................................................................................

..........................................................................................................

..........................................................................................................

# Vocabulary Review

**Word 1**    innovation

**Synonym**

---

**Word 2**    consequences

**Synonym**

---

**Word 3**    detrimental

**Antonym**

---

**Word 4**    ludicrous

**Antonym**

| | Active Participation | Interactive Reader | Critical Thinking Application | Week 18 Total |
|---|---|---|---|---|
| **TOTAL POINTS FOR WEEK 18** | | | | |

# Dottie:
## BELLE OF THE BALL GAME

By Hilary Mac Austin

## Build Background

Imagine a scene: Dottie Kamenshek, standing at home plate and eyeing the pitcher. It's a cool day in 1942 at a baseball diamond in her hometown of Cincinnati, Ohio, maybe with a light wind blowing in from left field. The high-school student is a good first-baseman and a solid hitter, so she isn't worried about what the pitcher might bring. The stands are filled with sports fans, families, and anyone who wants to see a good game. Women's softball is thriving in the 1940s.

Kamenshek was one of the best players in women's softball, but she had no way to make it a career. There weren't any professional softball or baseball teams for women. Kamenshek and other players like her had no idea their futures were about to change, and all because of a nervous chewing-gum **tycoon.**

Phillip K. Wrigley was worried about the future of professional baseball. It was the height of World War II, and most men were off fighting. Besides running Wrigley's Chewing Gum, Wrigley was the owner of the Chicago Cubs, and he was afraid Major League Baseball would be **disbanded.** Wrigley came up with an idea. He would form a professional women's league! The All-American Girls Professional Baseball League was born.

On May 17, 1943, 280 of the best women softball players in America gathered at Wrigley Field, the home of the Chicago Cubs. They were trying out for the newly-created league. Kamenshek was eighteen. Some

## Generate Questions

Dottie: Belle of the Ball Game

were as young as fifteen, and many had never been away from home before. They were awed by the famous ivy-covered walls of Wrigley Field and the huge stands. They were trying out for a *professional* baseball team, and they couldn't believe their luck.

After a day of slamming balls for home runs, diving for catches and making double plays, Kamenshek was picked to play first base on the Rockford Peaches where she would stay for most of the next ten years. The first year, the sixty players in the new league were paid between $45 and $85 a week, more than some of their fathers made.

At first, the game the women played was a combination of women's softball and men's baseball. The pitch was underhand, but runners could lead off and steal bases. Soon the game became more and more like men's baseball. The diamond was almost as large as in men's ball. The size of the ball got smaller, and pitchers began to throw overhand.

No matter how much the game grew to be like men's baseball, it was still being played by women, and in the 1940s that was a big deal. The organizers wanted good baseball without sacrificing the players' femininity. After ten tough hours of working out in spring training, the women went to "charm school" at night. They were taught how to apply lipstick, stand tall, and move gracefully—wearing high heels!

Dottie: Belle of the Ball Game

The uniform was also designed to be **feminine** and might have been the worst part of playing for the All-American League. It was a short, belted dress with shorts underneath—no help in the cold. "Maybe that's why we ran so fast," Kamenshek once joked.

These uniforms offered no protection when sliding into base. The players were tough, though. Kamenshek explained, "In the spring we [were] always hoping we'd develop **calluses.** If you got your skin toughened up, you were pretty lucky most of the year."

The players got better and the league became more popular, even after the war. By 1948 the Queens of Swat, as the press called them, ruled the Midwest. Almost a million people watched them play fast, hard baseball. "I think we proved we could play ball like the men," said Terry Donahue, a catcher for Peoria. "We couldn't throw as far or hit as hard, but we made all the plays."

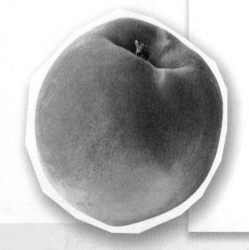

## Generate Questions

Kamenshek was a star. Wally Pipp, a famous player in the 1920s, called Kamenshek "the fanciest-fielding first baseman I've ever seen, man or woman." She played on seven All-Star teams and finished with a career batting average of .292, fourth in the league. After back injuries kept her out a season, Kamenshek came back for the 1953 season before retiring for good. Sadly, the league died the next year, partly because major league baseball was now on television, and the women's teams were running out of money.

For many years, few people knew about the glory days of the All-American Girls Professional Baseball League. That changed in 1992, when the movie *A League of Their Own* opened. Starring Tom Hanks, Geena Davis, and Madonna, it helped renew interest in the All-American Girls League. The character "Dottie" was modeled on several players, including Kamenshek. Several veteran players, then in their sixties and seventies, served as consultants. As a result, an important chapter in baseball history came to light. Dozens of articles, interviews, and websites have captured the stories of these talented women, and we can all learn the fascinating history of Dottie Kamenshek and the other Belles of the Ball Game.

## Verify Prediction

◯ CORRECT

◯ INCORRECT

## Summarize

.......................................................................................

.......................................................................................

.......................................................................................

.......................................................................................

.......................................................................................

# Vocabulary Review

**Word 1**

**Definition**

**Word 2**

**Definition**

**Word 3**

**Definition**

**Word 4**

**Definition**

| | Active Participation | Interactive Reader | Critical Thinking Application | Week 19 Total |
|---|---|---|---|---|
| **TOTAL POINTS FOR WEEK 19** | | | | |

Dottie: Belle of the Ball Game

# Where Have All the HONEYBEES GONE?

## By Arden Davidson

**Build Background**

**Word:** .........................................

**Definition:** ...............................

.......................................................

.......................................................

.......................................................

.......................................................

**Word:** .........................................

**Definition:** ...............................

.......................................................

.......................................................

.......................................................

.......................................................

What's bugging the bees? It's a mystery.

In late 2006, beekeepers around the world began to notice something strange. Adult worker bees were vanishing. They just disappeared, leaving only the queen bee and a few young bees. Without worker bees, colonies can't survive. Entomologists (scientists who study insects) called it "colony collapse disorder" (CCD). The numbers were staggering. Nearly one third of the hives in the United States were wiped out in the next few years, 70 percent in Canada.

Beekeepers expect that they'll lose a certain percent of their bees each winter to disease or other factors. They've suffered big losses before. In the 1980s, a **parasite** was making bees sick, and beekeepers knew how to deal with it. But CCD is different. A healthy colony of 70,000 bees can be—and often is—reduced to only a handful of bees in a few days. "There are no dead bodies," said May Berenbaum, a well-known entomologist who is searching for reasons bees are disappearing. "It's as if they're not coming home."

Why does it matter? Some might think it's a good thing—fewer bee stings in the backyard or at the pool. But the implications are far more serious. "I'm not a scientist, I'm a farmer, and I know one thing for certain," a cucumber grower told Congress in 2008. "No bees, no crops." At least ninety crops in the United States depend on bees to pollinate them. Almonds, strawberries, blueberries, cucumbers, apples,

## Generate Questions

.......................................................................................

.......................................................................................

.......................................................................................

.......................................................................................

.......................................................................................

peaches, beans, tomatoes, onions—the list seems endless. The annual value of such crops is more than $14 billion. The California almond industry is worth $2 billion a year and depends entirely on honeybees.

Then there are the products made from fruits, nuts, and beeswax. More than forty percent of the flavors in one brand of ice cream come from fruits and nuts that depend on honeybees. Beeswax is used to make skin creams, candles, furniture and shoe polish, and to keep cheese fresh. And of course, there's simple, delicious honey.

But the bee crisis is about much more than honey. "Honey is trivial compared with the importance of **pollination,**" Berenbaum said. Pollination is how plants make seeds. Apples, for example, start as flowers. Without bees, the flowers would stay flowers, but when bees gather nectar from apple blossoms on a tree, pollen sticks to their bodies. When they move to flowers on another tree, or rub up against another bee, that pollen moves to another flower, and apples are the result. This is called cross-pollination, and about eighty percent of the world's food supply relies on it.

So why are the worker bees not coming home? One possibility is that the bees' navigation system has been disturbed. "Honeybees have an incredibly sophisticated system for finding floral nectar . . . and having everybody come home safely," Berenbaum says. "And that's not what appears to be happening."

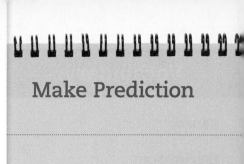

Make Prediction

## Vocabulary

**Word:** ........................

**Definition:** ........................

........................

........................

........................

**Word:** ........................

**Definition:** ........................

........................

........................

Many causes have been suspected, from cell phone radiation to climate change. **Pesticides,** poisons used to control insects, might be partly to blame. But bees killed by pesticides are usually found near the entrance to the hive, whereas bees with CCD leave and don't come back. Some pesticides have been known to affect insects' behavior rather than kill them outright. That appears to be what happens to bees with CCD, so pesticides still are a possible cause. So are diseases caused by very small organisms, including parasites and fungi.

Other theories are more far-fetched. Despite a lot of publicity suggesting that cell phone radiation could be causing CCD, there's no scientific evidence, according to Berenbaum. Climate change hasn't been proven to be a cause either. The likeliest cause is a combination of factors, but we don't yet know what they are.

Like humans, honeybees can suffer from stress, which makes them more **susceptible** to illness. Researchers have found that bees in colonies hit by CCD all suffered from poor nutrition and sometimes from drought. Without knowing exactly what's causing the decline in bee colonies, beekeepers have been working hard to keep their bees healthy. They've been controlling the insect pests that hurt bees, feeding their bees when honey in the hive is running low, and keeping pollen nearby.

## Generate Questions

........................

........................

........................

........................

Where Have All the Honeybees Gone?

There's a little good news. The number of bee colonies in the United States began to increase slightly in 2011. Still, losses are around thirty percent, much too high for beekeepers to stay in business year after year. The news is still grim in Europe. However, Berenbaum and other entomologists keep working to pinpoint the cause of CCD. In the meantime, what can we do to help honeybees?

Be careful about using pesticides in your yard or garden, especially in the middle of the day when bees are out looking for nectar. Plant flowers and bushes that bees like, such as red clover, foxglove, bee balm, and lavender, raspberries, and blackberries. Leave a few dandelions in the grass; bees love them.

Finally, buy local honey from beekeepers. That keeps more bees in your area. "And in addition," Berenbaum says, "you get the wonderful bonus of having this marvelous sweetener that is . . . absolutely delicious."

## Summarize

.......................................................................................................................

.......................................................................................................................

.......................................................................................................................

.......................................................................................................................

.......................................................................................................................

**Sentence**   My sister is _____ to colds.

**Sentence**   The gardener did not want to use _____ to kill the insects in his garden.

**Sentence**   Many trees need _____ in order to produce fruit.

**Sentence**   A _____ made the cat sick.

| | Active Participation | Interactive Reader | Critical Thinking Application | Week 20 Total |
|---|---|---|---|---|
| **TOTAL POINTS FOR WEEK 20** | | | | |

# The Mystery of STONEHENGE

By Leah Pietrusiak and Kathleen Thompson

## Build Background

121

A homely man with a rough beard set up his surveyor's instruments as the sun rose over a group of huge, pillar-like stones in the rolling countryside of southern England. The flat, thick rectangles of rock rose twenty feet into the air. Across the tops of these stones lay other huge stones. They formed an immense circle. At 108 feet in diameter, it was wider than a modern professional football field. As the shadows of the stones stretched long in the sunrise, it was easy to believe that the place held secrets and hidden powers.

Stonehenge is a megalith, an ancient stone monument. The **surveyor,** architect Inigo Jones, was more often found in London, designing buildings for King James I or arguing with playwright Ben Jonson. But the king had "suggested" that he survey Stonehenge, one of the great mysteries of the world. And in the 1600s, when kings suggested, subjects tended to hop to it.

Jones concluded that the mysterious prehistoric monument was a Roman temple. We now know these stones definitely are not the remains of a Roman temple. Archaeologists estimate that an ancient tribe began building Stonehenge on the Salisbury Plain about five thousand years ago, even before the Pyramids of Egypt were built. No one knows exactly who transported the massive stones, or how. But we can make some good guesses. Farmers grew grain and raised livestock in that area. Their only tools were made of stone or from animal bones.

## Generate Questions

The Mystery of Stonehenge

Around 3000 B.C., farming tribes constructed the first phase of Stonehenge—which actually had no stones. Stonehenge started as a six-foot ditch and an earth bank in the shape of a circle. An earth bank is formed by digging a ditch and then piling the earth into a mound next to it.

About five hundred years later, the first stones appeared at Stonehenge. Some historians believe chiefs from a rich tribe during the Bronze Age commissioned the construction of the stone structures. These leaders may be the people who were buried near Stonehenge.

Over the next thousand years, the structure was rebuilt in various ways. Because it took so long to build, different groups of people almost certainly used it in different ways, but the basic circle structure was unchanged. Stonehenge's circle shape is not unusual for that time period. Stone or earth bank circles appear all over southern England, and a thousand still remain. They might symbolize the sun, which is basic to life. Other theories are that over the five hundred years Stonehenge was built and added on to, it was used for religious ceremonies, for **pilgrimages,** or for observing the sun and moon.

Make Prediction

**Word:**

**Definition:**

**Word:**

**Definition:**

Astronomers have long discussed whether the stones are arranged to mark the summer and winter solstice. The summer solstice is around June 21 and is the longest day of the year, when the sun is furthest north in the sky. The winter solstice is just the opposite—around December 21 and the shortest day of the year, when the sun is furthest south in the sky.

Mysterious as the purpose—or purposes—of Stonehenge are, its construction is even more mysterious. The stones at Stonehenge are made up of two types, sarsens and bluestones. Boulders of sarsen, a kind of sandstone formed by a seabed seventy million years ago, were located about twenty-five miles north of Stonehenge. Sarsen boulders make up the outside circle and inner horseshoe shape. The bluestones, which make up some of the formations inside the main ring, are smaller, weighing about four tons on average. Some historians believe they came from the Preseli Mountains in Wales more than 130 miles away.

Moving either type of stone would have been an almost impossible feat. The architects of Stonehenge may have used heavy wooden sleds pulled by people or cattle. They may have built rafts to float the bluestones down the Bristol Channel. Some geologists now think glaciers, or huge sheets of ice, pushed the stones onto the Salisbury Plain where the Stonehenge builders found them.

## Generate Questions

Then the builders set the stones up in the middle of a field. The largest ones weigh about forty-five tons and stand almost thirty feet tall. Raising the huge vertical stones required tremendous **ingenuity,** but it is the top stones that astound us still. Archaeologists believe the builders first raised each lintel (top part of a doorway) by forcing a log underneath. Once the lintel was boosted up, they built a platform and started the process again until they reached the top. That's one possibility, but no one knows for sure. Like Inigo Jones, we keep looking for answers.

Stonehenge was abandoned more than 3,500 years ago. And today more than one million people visit its ruins each year. Some of its original stones have fallen or been stolen. And to preserve the site, visitors are forbidden to walk through the crop of towering stones anymore. In the year 2000, though, England allowed the public into the area for the summer solstice, in honor of the change of the **millennium.** The ancient stone circle has now seen five of them.

## Verify Prediction

◯ **CORRECT**

◯ **INCORRECT**

## Summarize

_____

_____

_____

_____

_____

**Word 1**

**Sentence**

**Word 2**

**Sentence**

**Word 3**

**Sentence**

**Word 4**

**Sentence**

| | Active Participation | Interactive Reader | Critical Thinking Application | Week 21 Total |
|---|---|---|---|---|
| **TOTAL POINTS FOR WEEK 21** | | | | |

# Savvy

By Ingrid Law

Part One

## Build Background

....................................................................

....................................................................

....................................................................

....................................................................

....................................................................

127

**Word:**

**Definition:**

**Word:**

**Definition:**

When my brother Fish turned thirteen, we moved to the deepest part of inland because of the hurricane and, of course, the fact that he'd caused it. I had liked living down south on the edge of land, next to the pushing-pulling waves. I had liked it with a mighty kind of liking, so moving had been hard—hard like the pavement the first time I fell off my pink two-wheeler and my palms burned like fire from all of the hurt just under the skin. But it was plain that Fish could live nowhere near or nearby or next to or close to or on or around any largish bodies of water. Water had a way of **triggering** my brother and making ordinary, everyday weather take a frightening turn for the worse.

Unlike any normal hurricane, Fish's birthday storm had started without warning. One minute, my brother was tearing paper from presents in our backyard near the beach; the next minute, both Fish and the afternoon sky went a funny and fearsome shade of gray. My brother gripped the edge of the picnic table as the wind kicked up around him, gaining momentum and ripping the wrapping paper out of his hands, sailing it high up in the sky with all the balloons and streamers roiling together and **disintegrating** like a birthday party in a blender. Groaning and cracking, trees shuddered and bent over double, uprooting and falling as easily as sticks in wet sand. Rain pelted us like

## Generate Questions

gravel thrown by a playground bully as windows shattered and shingles ripped off the roof. As the storm surged and the ocean waves tossed and churned, spilling raging water and debris farther and farther up the beach, Momma and Poppa grabbed hold of Fish and held on tight, while the rest of us ran for cover. Momma and Poppa knew what was happening. They had been expecting something like this and knew that they had to keep my brother calm and help him ride out this storm.

That hurricane had been the shortest on record, but to keep the coastal towns safe from our Fish, our family had packed up and moved deep inland, plunging into the very heart of the land and stopping as close to the center of the country as we could get. There, without big water to fuel big storms, Fish could make it blow and rain without so much heartache and ruin.

Settling directly between Nebraska and Kansas in a little place all our own, just off Highway 81, we were well beyond hollering distance from the nearest neighbor, which was the best place to be for a family like ours.

Monday through Wednesday, we called our thin stretch of land Kansaska. Thursday through Saturday, we called it Nebransas.

**Word:**

**Definition:**

**Word:**

**Definition:**

If it weren't for old Grandpa Bomba, Kansaska-Nebransas wouldn't even have existed for us to live there. When Grandpa wasn't a grandpa and was just instead a small-fry, hobbledehoy boy blowing out thirteen dripping candles on a **lopsided** cake, his savvy hit him hard and sudden—just like it did to Fish that day of the backyard birthday party and the hurricane—and the entire state of Idaho got made.

"Before I turned thirteen," he'd say, "Montana bumped dead straight into Washington, and Wyoming and Oregon shared a cozy border." The tale of Grandpa's thirteenth birthday had grown over the years just like the land he could move and stretch, and Momma just shook her head and smiled every time he'd start talking tall. But in truth, that young boy who grew up and grew old like wine and dirt, had been making new places whenever and wherever he pleased. That was Grandpa's savvy.

## Generate Questions

My savvy hadn't come along yet. But I was only two days away from my very own thirteen dripping candles—though *my* momma's cakes never lopped to the side or to the middle. Momma's cakes were perfect, just like Momma, because that was her savvy. Anything she made was perfect. Everything she did was perfect. Even when she messed up, Momma messed up perfectly.

"My savvy is going to be a good one," I told my brother Rocket. "I just know it."

"Girls don't get the powerful jujubes," said Rocket, running one hand through this dark shock of **unkempt** hair with a crackle of static. "Girls only get quiet, polite savvies—sugar and spice and everything humdrum savvies. It's boys who get the earthshaking kinds of savvy." Rocket and I both knew that there were plenty of girls climbing round our family tree that had strong and sturdy savvies, like Great-aunt Jules, who could step back twenty minutes in time every time she sneezed; our second cousin Olive, who could melt ice with a single red-hot stare.

## Summarize

...........................................................................................

...........................................................................................

...........................................................................................

...........................................................................................

...........................................................................................

# Vocabulary Review

**Word 1**

**Definition**

**Word 2**

**Definition**

**Word 3**

**Definition**

**Word 4**

**Definition**

| | Active Participation | Interactive Reader | Critical Thinking Application | Week 22 Total |
|---|---|---|---|---|
| **TOTAL POINTS FOR WEEK 22** | | | | |

● FICTION
● NONFICTION

# Savvy

**By Ingrid Law**

Part Two

## Build Background

**Word:**

**Definition:**

...........................................

...........................................

...........................................

**Word:**

**Definition:**

...........................................

...........................................

...........................................

Rocket was seventeen and full of junk that I wasn't allowed to say until I got much, much older. But he was electric through and through, and that had always gone to his head. For fun, Rocket would make my hair stand on end like he'd rubbed it with a balloon, or hit Fish with a wicked zap from the other side of the room. But Rocket could keep the lights on when the power went out, and our family sure liked that, especially the littler Beaumonts.

Rocket was the oldest, with Fish and me following after. Born only a year apart, Fish and I were nearly the same height and looked a lot alike, both with hair like sand and straw—hair like Momma's. But while I had Poppa's hazel eyes, Fish had Momma's ocean blue ones. It was as if we'd each taken a little bit of Momma, or a little bit of Poppa, and made the rest our own.

I wasn't the youngest or the smallest in the family; **broody** Samson was a dark and shadowy seven, and doll-faced Gypsy was three. It was Gypsy who started calling me Mibs, when my full name, Mississippi, became far too much for her toothsome toddler tongue to manage. But that had been a relief. That name had always followed me around like one of Fish's heavy storm clouds.

## Generate Questions

...........................................................................................

...........................................................................................

...........................................................................................

...........................................................................................

The itch and scritch of birthday buzz was about all I was feeling on the Thursday before the Friday before the Saturday I turned thirteen. Sitting at the dinner table, next to Poppa's empty chair and ready plate, I barely ate a bite.

I pushed the food around on my plate, ignoring my sister and daydreaming about what it would be like when I got my very own savvy, when the telephone rang right in the middle of pot roast, mashed potatoes, and mighty unpopular green beans. As Momma rose to answer, us kids, and Grandpa Bomba too, seized the chance to plop our mashers on top of our beans while Momma's back was turned.

We were all smiling to each other around the kitchen table at the smart way we'd taken care of those beans when Momma dropped the phone with a rattling clatter and a single sob—perfectly **devastated.**

"It's Poppa," Momma said in a choked voice, as her perfect features stretched and pinched.

"Momma?" Rocket ventured. The air around him crackled with static, and his T-shirt clung to him like socks to towels straight from the dryer. The lights in the house pulsed, and blue sparks popped and snapped at the tips of his nervous, twitching fingers.

Momma looked at Poppa's empty chair and waiting plate, then she turned to us, chin trembling, and told us about the accident on the highway. She told us how Poppa's car had gotten crushed up bad, like a pop can under a cowboy boot, and how he'd gone and forgotten to get out before it happened, landing himself in a room and a bed at Salina Hope Hospital, where now he lay broken and asleep, not able to wake up.

For half of a half of a half of a second I hated Poppa. I hated him for working so far away from home and for having to take the highway every day. I hated him for getting in that accident and for ruining our pot roast. Mostly, I realized that my perfect cake with its pink and yellow frosting was probably not going to get made, and I hated Poppa for wrecking my most important birthday before it even arrived.

## Generate Questions

Then I felt the burning shame of even having those thoughts about my good, sweet poppa and sank low in my chair. To make **amends** for my selfish feelings, I sat quietly and ate every last unwelcome green bean from beneath my mashed potatoes, as Fish's rain lashed against the windows and Rocket caused every lightbulb in the house to explode with a live-wired zing and a popping shatter, sending **shards** of glass tinkling to the floor and pitching the house into darkness.

Later that night, as I lay awake in the dark bedroom I shared with Gypsy, I listened to my sister's even breathing and to the steady patter of Fish's worried rain.

Momma and Rocket were leaving for Salina early in the morning and planning to stay in a motel near the hospital. I had begged to go, begged to go see Poppa and stay in a motel and get some of those little soaps all wrapped up in paper. But the rest of us had to stay at home with Grandpa. Rocket got to go because his electric touch was the only thing that could make the old station wagon run.

## Summarize

........................................................................................

........................................................................................

........................................................................................

........................................................................................

........................................................................................

# Vocabulary Review

**Sentence**   Ming was                          when he heard his brother was in the hospital.

**Sentence**   Dave swept up the broken glass so that the                wouldn't cut him.

**Sentence**   After fighting with his mother, he apologized to make                          .

**Sentence**   If a book or movie makes me sad, I can be a little                alone in my room.

| | Active Participation | Interactive Reader | Critical Thinking Application | Week 23 Total |
|---|---|---|---|---|
| **TOTAL POINTS FOR WEEK 23** | | | | |

# Savvy

Part Three

**By Ingrid Law**

## Build Background

Nobody had said anything about my birthday. Nobody had said much about much. I lay awake most of the night, unable to sleep, until Momma tiptoed in with the dawn to whisper a soft good-bye, kissing my cheek lightly with her perfect pink lips.

That Friday before my birthday, Fish was in charge of looking after Gypsy and Grandpa Bomba. It was my job to get Samson up and ready for school and to make sure we both made it up the three steep steps of the big orange bus that took Samson and me the fifteen miles to school in Hebron, Nebraska. Samson didn't say much waiting for the bus, but Samson never did.

When Samson and I got back home that afternoon, a shiny gold minivan was parked in front of our house and Fish was angrily blasting it clean with the garden hose. With its smiling angel air freshener dangling in the front window, I recognized the van immediately. It belonged to Miss Rosemary, the preacher's wife. Somehow, the news had already reached the preacher's wife about Poppa's accident and about the rest of us being on our own without a momma. Miss Rosemary had come to set things right.

## Generate Questions

She was perched up high, with a spray bottle cocked in one rubber-gloved hand and a rag held ready in the other. She was taking the jars from the tops of the cupboards and cleaning their dust with a wrinkle of her nose, squinting at the faded labels.

"Your mother should have called me the moment she found out about your poor father," Miss Rosemary said, dusting the last jar with a **flourish.** Satisfied with her work, she clasped both the spray bottle and the rag to her chest and closed her eyes as though she was praying for strength to clean up the whole wide world. When she reopened her eyes, she gave us a stern and **solemn** look.

"I ought to have been here sooner," she sighed.

"A little bird told me that tomorrow is *someone's* birthday," Miss Rosemary said with a quick, corner-of-the-eye glance from Gypsy to me as she cut a slab of meat loaf and placed it onto Grandpa Bomba's plate. The preacher's wife smiled down at the meat loaf, with its big, unfortunate, wormy onions and thin, dry layer of ketchup. I watched the knife as she cut another slice, and pretended that I hadn't heard her say anything.

**Word:**

**Definition:**

..............................................................

..............................................................

..............................................................

**Word:**

**Definition:**

..............................................................

..............................................................

..............................................................

Sitting at the table just then was like sitting in a pressure cooker—thanks to Fish; the air in the room went hot and **taut.** Only Gypsy reacted to Miss Rosemary, because she was three years old and didn't know yet what the rest of us Beaumonts knew about secrets—needing them, having them, or keeping them. Gypsy clapped her toddler hands together, eyes bright and eager in anticipation of balloons and sugar frosting.

"I thought," Miss Rosemary continued, apparently unaware of the tension—and the breeze. "I *thought* that a birthday party might help cheer everyone up a bit." Fish stared at the salt and pepper shakers in front of him, the good crystal ones that Momma never used but kept up high in the don't-touch-or-else cupboard. I could see him trying to get a good tight grip on his savvy.

"We'll have the party at the church, of course," the preacher's wife continued as though she'd not been interrupted. "It's rather short notice, but we can still invite all your church friends, Mibs, as well as anyone from school you'd like to ask."

"I don't have any friends, Miss Rosemary," I said, hoping that the truth might end the conversation.

## Generate Questions

..............................................................................................

..............................................................................................

..............................................................................................

..............................................................................................

..............................................................................................

"I'll show you. I'll get on the phone this evening and cook you up a fine party for tomorrow. Don't you worry, Mibs, I have *connections.*" Miss Rosemary pointed one finger up to the ceiling, though I guessed she was really pointing up toward heaven. Apparently she was going to get God to help her plan my party.

And I knew I wasn't the only one—I could feel Fish and Grandpa getting more and more nervous at all the talk of parties. Thirteen birthdays in the Beaumont family were **strictly** non-public affairs.

I woke up early on that Saturday morning of my thirteenth birthday and lay still and silent for a long, long while, just waiting. Nothing felt too different yet. I couldn't see through the ceiling or turn on my lamp with a blink or a wink. I couldn't float up off my mattress or make my pillow disappear.

I sighed and drum, drum, drummed my fingers against the pattern of my sheets. Nothing was happening. At least, not yet.

## Verify Prediction

○ CORRECT

○ INCORRECT

## Summarize

........................................................

........................................................

........................................................

........................................................

# Vocabulary Review

**Word 1**   flourish

**Synonym**

**Word 2**   strictly

**Synonym**

**Word 3**   solemn

**Antonym**

**Word 4**   taut

**Antonym**

| | Active Participation | Interactive Reader | Critical Thinking Application | Week 24 Total |
|---|---|---|---|---|
| **TOTAL POINTS FOR WEEK 24** | | | | |

# For the Love of the Game:
## Video Games Then and Now
By Troy Markham

## Build Background

In 1972, when Amy Hennig was just nine years old, the first video game, *Pong,* was invented. Hennig would later become a legendary game designer, but as a kid she had no such ideas. She just liked to play the games. "I was one of those kids who saved up any allowance I could and blew it all on the arcade," she said years later.

*Pong*'s tennis-game graphics consisted entirely of two white lines, or "paddles," that moved back and forth to hit a white square "ball." In **retrospect,** *Pong* was so simple it is laughable that so many people were taken by it. But the truth is no one had ever seen anything like it. The game cost a quarter to play, and consumers couldn't shovel them into the slots quickly enough. A new industry was born.

Although *Pong* looked nothing like the exciting visual dramas Hennig would later create as an adult, it made a big splash in entertainment culture. As Hennig played *Pong*—fascinated, eyes glued to the screen— the future of more exciting and **complicated** video games was forming in her mind.

## Generate Questions

For the Love of the Game: Video Games Then and Now

The arcade game *Pong* was developed by Atari engineer Nolan Bushnell, but like most inventions, earlier ideas paved the way. Engineer Ralph Baer had come up with a way to play games on a television set in 1969. A nuclear physicist had created a "video tennis game" on a computer in 1958 to entertain visitors to a scientific institute.

The seeds planted in Hennig's mind by *Pong* blossomed in 1977 when three things happened. The hugely popular movie *Star Wars* was released, showing what special effects could do for a great story. Next, Hennig discovered the game *Dungeons and Dragons.* It relied on imagination and strategy and allowed creative players to explore and compete in fantasy worlds. Finally, Atari released its 2600 video game system.

Atari had discovered that there was a market for home versions of video games. As consumers began to spend more time and money playing video games at home as well as on arcade machines, more creative engineers flocked to the industry. Hennig devoured these games, playing late into the night. "I had this moment where I realized this was a new medium and imagined what was possible with it," Hennig said. She couldn't help wondering if creative stories, such as those in *Star Wars* and *Dungeons and Dragons,* could be brought into video games.

The next big video game created a stir like no other. *Pac-Man,* designed by the Japanese company Namco in 1980, **transcended** the boundaries of previous games to become a cultural **icon.** Within a year, it was the best-selling arcade game in North America, bringing in over $1 billion in quarters. There were *Pac-Man* cartoons, lunch boxes, toys, and even a hit pop song about the game.

The *Pac-Man* phenomenon changed the model for creating video games. Suddenly video games were big business. Also, unlike the space-shooter games at the time, *Pac-Man* featured characters. That innovation attracted women to video games and is now practically essential to modern games.

Hennig is considered a video game visionary as well as a pioneer in an industry dominated by males. Her contributions have been admired and closely followed by her peers. In 2010 her game *Uncharted 2: Among Thieves* won Game of the Year at the Game Developers Choice Awards.

Today's video games for home computers, gaming systems, and hand-held devices bear little resemblance to those Hennig helped design in the 1990s. Games were developed on computer cartridges with very little memory. "You couldn't do voices," Hennig recalled. Modern backgrounds and graphics are very realistic, with the kinds of fantastic visuals expected from blockbuster movies. Programmers, artists,

## Generate Questions

directors, music composers, mathematicians, animation specialists, and writers are coordinated through many stages of development.

This is where Hennig's genius and creativity come in. Unlike some earlier game designers, she does not focus solely on graphics and action. She believes the storyline is the most crucial element to video games. Hennig did not get a degree in programming or engineering. Instead she graduated with a degree in English literature and then went to film school. Her background in these areas reflects a focus on atmosphere, plot, and character in her video games.

"Everything I learned as an undergraduate with English literature and in film school about editing and shots and the language of film has come into play, but in a way I couldn't possibly have planned," Hennig said. She continued to write and direct games, winning accolades (awards and congratulations) from players and other game creators. Using her background as a writer, she developed games as series in which the storyline and characters continue from one game to the next. Some of her most popular creations are the *Legacy of Kain* series, *Uncharted* series, and *Jak and Daxter* series.

"When people play the *Uncharted* games they just get caught up," Hennig says. "A lot of it has to do with wanting to see what happens next because you care about the characters."

## Summarize

...................................................................................................

...................................................................................................

...................................................................................................

...................................................................................................

...................................................................................................

# Vocabulary Review

**Word 1**

**Definition**

**Word 2**

**Definition**

**Word 3**

**Definition**

**Word 4**

**Definition**

| | Active Participation | Interactive Reader | Critical Thinking Application | Week 25 Total |
|---|---|---|---|---|
| **TOTAL POINTS FOR WEEK 25** | | | | |

For the Love of the Game: Video Games Then and Now

# Millions of Rosies

*By Hilary Mac Austin*

We Can Do It!

## Build Background

**Word:**

**Definition:**

**Word:**

**Definition:**

In the shipyards of Richmond, California, the **gargantuan** steel skeleton of a cargo ship soared high overhead, and deafening clanks, crashes, roars, whirrs, and booms filled the air. Workers swarmed over the ship, welding and riveting sheets of steel. After Japan attacked the United States at Pearl Harbor in 1941 and war was declared, workers flooded Richmond to build ships for the war effort. Within two years, the population quadrupled, and thousands of those workers were women. The women entering this place might have been a little intimidated at first, but they came in the millions.

During World War II, women joined the American workforce in record numbers. While they worked in the traditionally female professions such as clerk, secretary, nurse, or receptionist, they also toiled in jobs that were considered traditionally male, including welder, riveter, fork lift driver, crane operator, and pilot. Women war workers assembled dangerous **munitions,** constructed the new B-17 bombers, and built enormous battleships and submarines. In so doing they helped the United States and its allies win the war.

## Generate Questions

Of course women had always worked, particularly poor and minority women. When the war started, those women moved into higher-paying jobs men had previously held. But the government needed so many workers it had to convince middle-class women to enter the workforce. In order to get women into the factories, the government started a propaganda campaign to encourage women to become war workers. One result of the campaign was a poster that still influences women today.

The woman staring out of the poster looks glamorous, strong, and determined. She wears a bandana to keep her hair out of her eyes. She's rolling up the sleeves of her work shirt, ready to "go at it" and do the work of saving the nation. "We Can Do It!" screams the poster. Its message is that the women of American—together—can run the factories and build the ships and planes needed to win the war. The woman came to be called Rosie the Riveter. (A riveter is a worker who bolts pieces of steel together.)

Make Prediction

The real person who inspired that poster, Geraldine Doyle, was only seventeen years old when she went to work in a metal factory in Ann Arbor, Michigan, where a photographer snapped her picture. Ironically, Doyle worked at the factory for only a couple of weeks. She had heard that another worker had badly hurt her hands a few weeks before. Doyle played a cello and didn't want to hurt *her* hands, so she quit and went to work at a soda fountain and bookstore. Before long, she married a dental student and raised four children. Doyle had no idea she was the face of Rosie the Riveter until 1982, when she read an article about the poster.

Rosary Cooper was another Rosie—one of many. She may not have inspired a **propaganda** poster, but she actually did the dangerous factory work. In fact, like many other women, Cooper was looking for the most dangerous job; it was a challenge, and it paid better.

"When I first went to the shipyard I was a file clerk," Cooper said many years later. "And then they were training the women on the cranes. . . .  I'm not going to say I wasn't afraid, I was. But I wasn't going to give [the men] the benefit of the doubt of knowing it. . . .  I kept going up until I got to be a first mate's crane operator on the 20 ton crane. That's the one that lays the keels for the submarines, the cradle, and the engines, the torpedo tubes, anything like that. I worked on those 110 feet in the air." One hundred ten feet is about as high as a ten-story building!

## Generate Questions

Before the war, 12 million women were in the workforce; by the end of the war there were 18 million. Before the war, women made up 8 percent of the number of people making **durable goods** in the United States. At the end of the war, they made up 25 percent.

When the war ended in 1945, the men came back from fighting and needed employment. Women were expected to give up their jobs and go back home or into service jobs, since the military no longer needed them to build ships and planes. While some women stayed in the workforce, the majority of middle-class women went home to raise children and become involved in their communities.

But American women didn't forget that they had taken on the heavy load of war work, and they didn't forget the slogan "We Can Do It." Rosie the Riveter continued to inspire generations of women long after the war had ended. Women had fueled the wartime economy, had entered the military, and acquired new skills and confidence. They knew they could do whatever was asked of them. Women in later years could look at the poster and think, "If women could do that hard work during World War II, then I can do it now."

## Verify Prediction

○ **CORRECT**

○ **INCORRECT**

## Summarize

.....................................................................

.....................................................................

.....................................................................

.....................................................................

.....................................................................

**Sentence**   The _____ in the kitchen were a refrigerator and a dishwasher.

**Sentence**   The soldiers needed the _____ to be in good working order so they could fight the war.

**Sentence**   The _____ machine made a very loud noise.

**Sentence**   The magazine published the _____ to convince people to volunteer for service.

| | Active Participation | Interactive Reader | Critical Thinking Application | Week 26 Total |
|---|---|---|---|---|
| **TOTAL POINTS FOR WEEK 26** | | | | |

# Einstein's Brain
## Takes a Road Trip

By Leah Pietrusiak

## Build Background

**Word:** ........................................

**Definition:** ................................

..............................................................

..............................................................

..............................................................

..............................................................

**Word:** ........................................

**Definition:** ................................

..............................................................

..............................................................

..............................................................

..............................................................

Dr. Thomas Harvey panted as he trudged up the basement steps. He was old, and the box he was carrying was heavy. He stepped out of the shadows, set the cardboard box down, and pulled out two ordinary glass canning jars. The contents were far from ordinary, though. They were parts of the brain of Albert Einstein, one of the greatest geniuses in history.

Harvey had been toting the jars of brain tissue around for forty years. He was the **pathologist** who had performed the autopsy (examination after death) on Einstein after the great thinker died in a New Jersey hospital in 1955. Harvey removed the brain to examine it. But instead of putting it back in Einstein's skull, as he was expected to, he put it in a jar of formaldehyde (a preservative) and took it home.

Einstein's body was to be cremated, and Harvey couldn't bear the thought of losing the brain. He lost his job over the strange episode, but Harvey wanted to advance the cause of science. Over the years he sent sections of brain tissue to scientists to examine. They wanted to see whether there was something different about Einstein's brain that had made him so brilliant.

## Generate Questions

....................................................................................................................

....................................................................................................................

....................................................................................................................

....................................................................................................................

....................................................................................................................

....................................................................................................................

But now Harvey thought that Einstein's granddaughter in California might like to have the brain. So he and a writer, who'd agreed to drive him, loaded up the Buick for a road trip across the country. Einstein's brain rode in a Tupperware bowl in the trunk.

Studying Einstein's brain has been quite a road trip for scientists. At first there was little to go on. Some researchers believe that brain size could be related to intelligence. But Einstein's brain weighed less than a normal male brain, and it had the normal number of neurons. Studies also showed unusual **grooves** in areas that are linked to ability in mathematics and spatial reasoning, an ability to visualize and understand concepts. However, there was still no data to explain the kind of genius that produced theories that eventually allowed people to travel into outer space.

The respected scientist Marian Diamond, of the University of California at Berkeley, received sections of Einstein's brain tissue in a mayonnaise jar, which Dr. Harvey sent by mail. Her research eventually shed light not only on Einstein's mental abilities but on how the brain itself works. Diamond wanted to see if Einstein's brain cells, called neurons, were bigger or more numerous than normal. They weren't.

Make Prediction

Then she noticed that the brain had an unusually high number of glia cells. These cells wrap around neurons to feed them and act as protection, like bubble wrap. Diamond discovered the most glia cells in the area of Einstein's brain that governs imagery and **complex** thinking. That was interesting, but scientists didn't know what to make of it. Up to that point, they believed glia had no role in communicating with other brain cells. Neurons did the hard work, and Einstein's brain had a normal number of neurons.

Finally in the mid-2000s, a new discovery changed brain science. It also made sense of Diamond's discovery. Researchers already knew glia didn't release electrical impulses like neurons did. But did astrocytes (a type of glia cell so named because they look like stars) communicate with each other some other way?

The answer turned out to be yes. They speak a special language of chemical messages. Using a chemical that glows bright green when calcium is added to it, researchers found that astrocytes send chemical messages coded in calcium. When researchers dropped a neurotransmitter into a Petri dish containing astrocytes, bright green raced through the astrocytes, signaling information transfer. It looked like a secret was being whispered from one end of a classroom to another!

## Generate Questions

Einstein's Brain Takes a Road Trip

Then they wanted to test whether astrocytes ever sent messages to neurons, not just each other. Researchers added a neuron to the dish. They saw, when a calcium message reached the space between two neurons, there was a change in the electrical signal that one neuron sent to the other.

Though scientists don't know for sure what messages glia are helping to pass on, they now know glia do more than pad brain cells. It's possible that the large number of glia in Einstein's brain helped him process ideas faster and understand more complex concepts. It's also possible that the grooves in his brain created denser areas of neuron and glial cells, making it easier for them to communicate.

Harvey and the writer made it to California, but Einstein's granddaughter didn't want the brain. So they drove back across the country, with Einstein's brain in the trunk of the Buick. Harvey returned it to Princeton Hospital in Princeton, New Jersey. He didn't live to see what ultimately was learned from the brain he lugged around for forty years, but he would have felt **vindicated.** Even after his death, Einstein was unlocking scientific mysteries.

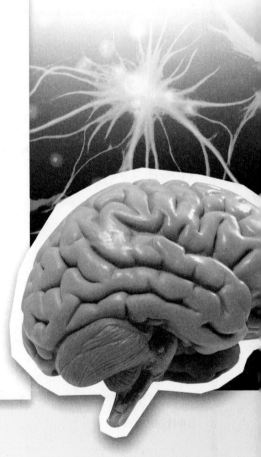

Verify Prediction

◯ CORRECT

◯ INCORRECT

## Summarize

.....................................................................................

.....................................................................................

.....................................................................................

.....................................................................................

.....................................................................................

# Vocabulary Review

## Word 1

**Sentence**

## Word 2

**Sentence**

## Word 3

**Sentence**

## Word 4

**Sentence**

| | Active Participation | Interactive Reader | Critical Thinking Application | Week 27 Total |
|---|---|---|---|---|
| **TOTAL POINTS FOR WEEK 27** | | | | |

# The SUPER BOWL

## By Dennis Fertig

## Build Background

**Word:**
........................................................

**Definition:**
........................................................

........................................................

........................................................

**Word:**
........................................................

**Definition:**
........................................................

........................................................

........................................................

You don't have to be a sports fan to answer this question: What is the biggest day in American sports? It's the Super Bowl. And it keeps getting bigger every year.

The Super Bowl is more than just a football game, although there have been some great games since the first one in January 1967. It's a media event that brings in millions of dollars for television networks and advertisers. With powerful athletes eager to crush their rivals and blockbuster halftime shows featuring such stars as Michael Jackson, the Rolling Stones, Paul McCartney, and Madonna, even people who don't watch much football tune in to "the big game."

The commercials alone get as much publicity as the game. One 30-second ad cost an average of $3.5 million in 2012, compared to $40,000 in 1967. All that money does pay off, though, because the number of viewers keeps increasing. A record 111.3 million people watched the 2012 Super Bowl between the New England Patriots and the New York Giants.

In contrast, the first championship game in January 1967 was a fairly quiet affair. Ticket prices were $12 compared to the average $3,000 in recent games. Although a record 65 million watched that first championship game on television, there were so many empty seats in the stadium that television producers asked fans to move closer together. It wasn't even officially called the Super Bowl yet.

## Generate Questions

................................................................................

................................................................................

................................................................................

................................................................................

The Super Bowl

That first game was between the Green Bay Packers—champions of the powerful National Football League (NFL) —and the Kansas City Chiefs—champions of the American Football League (AFL). As expected, the Packers, coached by Vince Lombardi, easily beat the Chiefs 35–10. Three years later, Lombardi's name was **inscribed** on the Super Bowl trophy that the winning team receives to this day.

The third Championship Game was officially named the Super Bowl, and that might be when Super Bowl media hype began. Even though NFL champion Baltimore Colts (later the Indianapolis Colts) were heavily favored to beat the AFL's New York Jets, the Jets' quarterback Joe Namath outrageously **guaranteed** that his team would win. Then, in a shocking surprise, the Jets did exactly that! And when the AFL celebrated victory again in the fourth Super Bowl, doubts about the AFL's inferiority were erased, and the game evolved into America's favorite sporting event. The two leagues evolved too, eventually merging into what is now known as the NFL. The NFL is split into two conferences with the champions of each conference competing in the Super Bowl at the end of the season.

Make Prediction

**Word:**
.................................

**Definition:**
.................................

.................................

.................................

.................................

.................................

**Word:**
.................................

**Definition:**
.................................

.................................

.................................

.................................

While some Super Bowls have been boring, with one team so dominating another that there's little excitement, there have been plenty of great games. One was Super Bowl X in 1976, a classic quarterback duel between Pittsburgh's Terry Bradshaw and Dallas's Roger Staubach. The two teams were bitter rivals, and the match-up exceeded all expectations.

With only four minutes in the game and the Steelers leading 15–10, Bradshaw threw a long pass to receiver Lynn Swann for a 64-yard touchdown—a second before a Cowboys defender knocked Bradshaw unconscious with a helmet-to-helmet hit. In spite of a drive by Staubach to the end zone in the final minutes, the Steelers won 21–10. Swann's acrobatic catch still shows up in photos of the best plays of the Super Bowl.

Another match-up makes every list of the best Super Games ever. In 2008 the New York Giants upset the heavily favored New England Patriots 17–14. With just two minutes and forty-two seconds left, Giants' quarterback Eli Manning and receiver David Tyrell snuffed out the Patriots' hopes. Tyrell made a wildly **unconventional** catch, clutching the ball against his helmet for a touchdown to win the game.

## Generate Questions

.................................................................................

.................................................................................

.................................................................................

.................................................................................

.................................................................................

Four years later in Super Bowl XLVI, the Patriots had a chance to even the score with the Giants. The game on February 5, 2012, was another match-up between Tom Brady and Eli Manning. It was the most-watched program in television history. Thirty-three percent of the American population tuned in.

After a strong start by the Giants, Brady fired one quick pass after another in the last few minutes of the first half, scoring a touchdown with eight seconds to go. Near the end of the second half with only a few minutes left, the Patriots led 17–15. Victory over their upstart rival was in sight.

But suddenly it was 2008 all over again. Led by Manning, the Giants launched another comeback, scoring with 57 seconds left. Fans cheered or wept, and another great Super Bowl went into the record books.

Why does America go a little bit crazy on Super Bowl Sunday? Maybe because it's entertaining, it's a physical game of athletic talent and strategy, it's big and flashy, and it's profitable. In other words, it's **quintessentially** American.

## Summarize

.......................................................................................

.......................................................................................

.......................................................................................

.......................................................................................

.......................................................................................

**Word 1**

**Definition**

**Word 2**

**Definition**

**Word 3**

**Definition**

**Word 4**

**Definition**

| | Active Participation | Interactive Reader | Critical Thinking Application | Week 28 Total |
|---|---|---|---|---|
| **TOTAL POINTS FOR WEEK 28** | | | | |

The Super Bowl

# A Remarkable Adventure

By Jack Prelutsky

**Purpose for Reading**

**Build Background**

## Vocabulary

**Word:**

**Definition:**

**Word:**

**Definition:**

**Word:**

**Definition:**

I was at my bedroom table

with a notebook open wide,

when a giant anaconda

started winding up my side,

I was filled with apprehension

and retreated down the stairs,

to be greeted at the bottom

by a dozen grizzly bears.

We **tumultuously** tussled

till I managed to get free,

then I saw, with **trepidation,**

there were tigers after me,

I could feel them growing closer,

I was quivering with fear,

then I blundered into quicksand

and began to disappear.

A Remarkable Adventure

I was rescued by an eagle

that descended from the skies

to embrace me with its talons,

to my terror and surprise,

but that raptor lost its purchase

when a blizzard made me sneeze,

and it dropped me in a thicket

where I battered both my knees.


I was suddenly surrounded

by a troop of savage trolls,

who **maliciously** informed me

they would toast me over coals,

I was lucky to elude them

when they briefly looked away—

that's the reason why my homework

isn't here with me today.

Speaker

○ FIRST PERSON

○ SECOND PERSON

○ THIRD PERSON

Visualization

A Remarkable Adventure

**For this week's Readers' Theater, think about how you met each expectation. Then circle a score for each.**

| Expectation | I *always* did this. | I *usually* did this. | I *sometimes* did this. | I *never* did this. |
|---|---|---|---|---|
| I spoke clearly when it was my turn to read my lines. | 4 | 3 | 2 | 1 |
| I worked well with my class to practice my lines. | 4 | 3 | 2 | 1 |
| I listened to others so that we spoke together on group lines. | 4 | 3 | 2 | 1 |
| I highlighted my lines so I knew when to speak. | 4 | 3 | 2 | 1 |
| I held the script so people could hear me (I didn't hide behind the script or look at the floor). | 4 | 3 | 2 | 1 |
| I used my voice to help people understand the poem. | 4 | 3 | 2 | 1 |

| | Active Participation | Interactive Reader | Critical Thinking Application | Week 29 Total |
|---|---|---|---|---|
| **TOTAL POINTS FOR WEEK 29** | | | | |

# Simile:
# WILLOW
# *and*
# GINKGO

## By Eve Merriam

### Purpose for Reading

### Build Background

**Word:**

**Definition:**

**Word:**

**Definition:**

**Word:**

**Definition:**

The willow is like an **etching,**

Fine-lined against the sky.

The ginkgo is like a **crude** sketch,

Hardly worthy to be signed.

The willow's music is like a soprano,

Delicate and thin.

The ginkgo's tune is like a chorus

With everyone joining in.


The willow is sleek as a velvet-nosed calf,

The ginkgo is leathery as an old bull.

The willow's branches are like silken thread;

The ginkgo's like stubby rough wool.

Simile: Willow and Ginkgo

The willow is like a **nymph** with streaming hair;

Wherever it grows, there is green and gold and fair.

The willow dips to the water,

Protected and precious, like the king's favorite daughter.


The ginkgo forces its way through gray concrete;

Like a city child, it grows up in the street.

Thrust against the metal sky,

Somehow it survives and even thrives.

*My eyes feast upon the willow,*

*But my heart goes to the ginkgo.*

Simile: Willow and Ginkgo

Theme

Speaker

○ FIRST PERSON

○ SECOND PERSON

○ THIRD PERSON

Visualization

# Self-Evaluation

**For this week's Readers' Theater, think about how you met each expectation. Then circle a score for each.**

| Expectation | I *always* did this. | I *usually* did this. | I *sometimes* did this. | I *never* did this. |
|---|---|---|---|---|
| I spoke clearly when it was my turn to read my lines. | 4 | 3 | 2 | 1 |
| I worked well with my class to practice my lines. | 4 | 3 | 2 | 1 |
| I listened to others so that we spoke together on group lines. | 4 | 3 | 2 | 1 |
| I highlighted my lines so I knew when to speak. | 4 | 3 | 2 | 1 |
| I held the script so people could hear me (I didn't hide behind the script or look at the floor). | 4 | 3 | 2 | 1 |
| I used my voice to help people understand the poem. | 4 | 3 | 2 | 1 |

| | Active Participation | Interactive Reader | Critical Thinking Application | Week 30 Total |
|---|---|---|---|---|
| **TOTAL POINTS FOR WEEK 30** | | | | |

Simile: Willow and Ginkgo

# Oranges

## By Gary Soto

## Purpose for Reading

## Build Background

## Vocabulary

**Word:**

**Definition:**

**Word:**

**Definition:**

**Word:**

**Definition:**

The first time I went out
With a girl, I was thirteen,
Cold, and weighted down
With two oranges in my jacket.
December. Frost cracking
Beneath my steps, my breath
Before me, then gone,
As I walked toward
Her house, the one whose
**Porch** light burned yellow
Night and day, in any weather.
A dog barked at me, until
She came out pulling
On her gloves, face bright
With makeup. I smiled,
Touched her shoulder, and led
Her down the street, across
A used car lot and a line
Of newly planted trees,
Until we were standing
In front of a drugstore.
We entered, the tiny bell
Bringing a saleslady
Down a narrow aisle of goods.
I turned to the candies
**Tiered** like bleachers,
And asked what she wanted—
Light in her eyes, a smile
Starting at the corners

178                                                    Oranges

Of her mouth. I fingered
A nickel in my pocket,
And when she lifted a chocolate
That cost a dime,
I didn't say anything.
I took the nickel from
My pocket, then an orange,
And set them quietly on
The counter. When I looked up,
The lady's eyes met mine,
And held them, knowing
Very well what it was all about,
Love, I mean.

Outside the drugstore,
A few cars **hissing** past,
Fog hanging like old
Coats between the wintery trees.
I took my girl's hand
In mine for two short blocks,
Then released it to let
Her unwrap her chocolate.
I peeled my orange
That was so bright against
The gray of December
That, from some distance,
Someone might have thought
I was making a fire in my hands.

## Stanza

## Theme

## Speaker

◯ FIRST PERSON

◯ SECOND PERSON

◯ THIRD PERSON

## Visualization

Oranges

# Self-Evaluation

**For this week's Readers' Theater, think about how you met each expectation. Then circle a score for each.**

| Expectation | I *always* did this. | I *usually* did this. | I *sometimes* did this. | I *never* did this. |
|---|---|---|---|---|
| I spoke clearly when it was my turn to read my lines. | 4 | 3 | 2 | 1 |
| I worked well with my class to practice my lines. | 4 | 3 | 2 | 1 |
| I listened to others so that we spoke together on group lines. | 4 | 3 | 2 | 1 |
| I highlighted my lines so I knew when to speak. | 4 | 3 | 2 | 1 |
| I held the script so people could hear me (I didn't hide behind the script or look at the floor). | 4 | 3 | 2 | 1 |
| I used my voice to help people understand the poem. | 4 | 3 | 2 | 1 |

| | Active Participation | Interactive Reader | Critical Thinking Application | Week 31 Total |
|---|---|---|---|---|
| TOTAL POINTS FOR WEEK 31 | | | | |

Oranges

# Caged Bird

By Maya Angelou

## Purpose for Reading

## Build Background

..........................................
..........................................
..........................................
..........................................

## Rhyme

◯ YES      ◯ NO

## Vocabulary

**Word:**

**Definition:**

**Word:**

**Definition:**

**Word:**

**Definition:**

A free bird leaps
on the back of the wind
and floats downstream
till the **current** ends
and dips his wing
in the orange sun rays
and dares to claim the sky.

But a bird that **stalks**
down his narrow cage
can seldom see through
his bars of **rage**
his wings are clipped and
his feet are tied
so he opens his throat to sing.

The caged bird sings
with a fearful trill
of things unknown
but longed for still
and his tune is heard
on the distant hill
for the caged bird
sings of freedom.

Caged Bird

The free bird thinks of another breeze
and the trade winds soft through the sighing trees
and the fat worms waiting on a dawn-bright lawn
and he names the sky his own
But a caged bird stands on the grave of dreams
his shadow shouts on a nightmare scream
his wings are clipped and his feet are tied
so he opens his throat to sing.

The caged bird sings
with a fearful trill
of things unknown
but longed for still
and his tune is heard
on the distant hill
for the caged bird
sings of freedom.

Caged Bird

## Stanza

## Theme

### Speaker

- ⚪ FIRST PERSON
- ⚪ SECOND PERSON
- ⚪ THIRD PERSON

## Visualization

# Self-Evaluation

**For this week's Readers' Theater, think about how you met each expectation. Then circle a score for each.**

| Expectation | I *always* did this. | I *usually* did this. | I *sometimes* did this. | I *never* did this. |
|---|---|---|---|---|
| I spoke clearly when it was my turn to read my lines. | 4 | 3 | 2 | 1 |
| I worked well with my class to practice my lines. | 4 | 3 | 2 | 1 |
| I listened to others so that we spoke together on group lines. | 4 | 3 | 2 | 1 |
| I highlighted my lines so I knew when to speak. | 4 | 3 | 2 | 1 |
| I held the script so people could hear me (I didn't hide behind the script or look at the floor). | 4 | 3 | 2 | 1 |
| I used my voice to help people understand the poem. | 4 | 3 | 2 | 1 |

| | Active Participation | Interactive Reader | Critical Thinking Application | Week 32 Total |
|---|---|---|---|---|
| **TOTAL POINTS FOR WEEK 32** | | | | |

Caged Bird

# Reading Log

**Name** _____ **Date** _____

| Start date | End date | Title | Author | How would you rate this book? Why? |
|---|---|---|---|---|
| | | | | |
| | | | | |
| | | | | |
| | | | | |
| | | | | |
| | | | | |
| | | | | |
| | | | | |

# Reading Log

**Name** _____ **Date** _____

| Start date | End date | Title | Author | How would you rate this book? Why? |
|---|---|---|---|---|
| | | | | |
| | | | | |
| | | | | |
| | | | | |
| | | | | |
| | | | | |
| | | | | |
| | | | | |

# Glossary

Use this glossary to pronounce and understand the meanings of the vocabulary words. The part of speech, such as *adj.* for **adjective** or *v.* for **verb,** shows how the vocabulary word is used in the selection it appears in. Page numbers in parentheses tell where to find the word in your Interactive Reader.

# A

**aggressive** (ə **gre** siv) *adj.* fast-moving, strong or intense (p. 22)

**agitated** (**aj** ə **tāt** əd) *adj.* irritated, upset (p. 68)

**amends** (ə **menz**) *n.* something you do to make up for a mistake; apologies (p. 137)

**analyze** (**a** nə līz) *v.* to study, figure out (p. 33)

**ancient** (**ān** chənt) *v.* belonging to a time in the past, early in history (p. 38)

**anticipate** (an **ti** si **pāt**) *v.* expect or predict (p. 62)

**appalling** (ə **pawl** ing) *adj.* very bad, terrible (p. 86)

# B

**bellow** (**be** lō) *v.* yell loudly (p. 95)

**braying** (**brā** ing) *v.* yelling in a loud, unpleasant way (p. 8)

**broody** (**broo** dē) *adj.* gloomy, moody (p. 134)

# C

**calluses** (**ka** lus əz) *n.* hard, thick areas of skin (p. 112)

**chances are** (**chans** iz ar) it's very likely, it's almost certain (p. 80)

**competitors** (com **pe** tə tərz) *n.* people who take part in a contest (p. 40)

## Pronunciation Key

The following symbols are used throughout this glossary.

| a | ask | e | bed | ō | over | ow | now | ə | about |
|---|-----|---|-----|---|------|-----|-----|---|-------|
| ā | ate |   | bread | u | but |   | about |   | kitten |
|   | eight | i | it |   | what | oy | boy |   | Canada |
|   | pain | ī | ice |   | other |   | oil |   | lemon |
| ē | pizza |   | tie | aw | awful | oo | book |   | circus |
|   | each |   | why |   | ball |   | pull |   | wanted |
|   | mini | o | on |   | auto | ōō | pool |   |  |
|   | many |   | father |   | soft |   | blue |   |  |
|   | feet |   | not |   |  |   |  |   |  |

Syllables that are underlined and in bold are stressed the most, such as **ak** in **reaction** (rē **ak shun**).

Syllables that are stressed a little but not as much as another syllable are in bold, such as **shun** in **reaction.**

# Glossary

**complex** (kom **pleks**) *adj.* complicated, not simple (p. 160)

**complicated** (**kom** pli **kā** təd) *adj.* difficult to understand or explain (p. 146)

**consequences** (**kon** si kwen səz) *n.* the results of an action or an event (p. 105)

**contagious** (kon **tā** jus) *adj.* easily spread from one person to another (p. 74)

**cowlick** (**kow** lik) *n.* small bunch of hair that sticks up and won't stay flat (p. 92)

**cringed** (krinjd) *v.* shrank back because of shock or fear (p. 16)

**crucial** (**krōō** shəl) *adj.* extremely important (p. 149)

**crude** (krōō d) *adj.* very simple (p. 174)

**current** (**ku** rent) *n.* continuous movement of water or air in one direction (p. 182)

# D

**desperately** (**des** pə rit lē) *adv.* urgently, frantically (p. 2)

**detrimental** (**de** trə **men** təl) *adj.* harmful (p. 107)

**devastated** (**de** və **stā** təd) *adj.* extremely pained and upset (p. 135)

**disbanded** (dis **ban** dəd) *adj.* ended, broken up (p. 110)

**disintegrating** (dis **in** tə **grā** ting) *v.* falling apart into very small pieces (p. 128)

**durable goods** (**dur** ə bəl **goodz**) products that last a long time, such as refrigerators or airplanes (p. 155)

# E

**eager** (**ē** gər) *adj.* very excited about, enthusiastic (p. 64)

**elated** (i **lā** təd) *adj.* very happy, excited (p. 34)

**epic** (**e** pik) *adj.* impressively great (p. 27)

**etching** (**e** ching) *n.* delicate picture made by rubbing ink on a carving and then pressing it onto paper (p. 174)

**expend** (ik **spend**) *v.* use up (p. 95)

# F

**fanfare** (**fan** fār) *n.* noisy public display (p. 99)

**fare** (fār) *n.* food, meals (p. 100)

**feats** (fētz) *n.* acts of strength (p. 70)

**feminine** (**fe** mə nin) *adj.* relating to women or girls (p. 112)

**flourish** (**fluh** rish) *n.* a showy or dramatic gesture (p. 141)

**frontier** (frun **tir**) *n.* unsettled country or land, territory (p. 98)

# G

**gargantuan** (gor **gan** ch$\overline{oo}$ ən) *adj.* huge and bulky (p. 152)

**garlands** (**gar** ləndz) *n.* woven chains of leaves or flowers worn for celebrating or decorating (p. 39)

**grooves** (gr$\overline{oo}$ vz) *n.* long, narrow, low areas on a surface (p. 159)

**gruel** (**gr$\overline{oo}$** əl) *n.* very thin oatmeal boiled in water (p. 44)

**guaranteed** (gar in **tēd**) *v.* promised that something would happen or be done (p. 165)

# H

**hardened** (**har** dənd) *adj.* unfeeling, not concerned with the suffering of others (p. 46)

**hissing** (**hi** sing) *v.* making a sharp swishing sound (p. 179)

# I

**icon** (**ī** kon) *n.* a person or thing people respect very much (p. 148)

**immortal** (i **mor** təl) *adj.* able to live forever, cannot die (p. 76)

**impressions** (im **pre** shənz) *n.* ideas, feelings, or opinions of someone or something (p. 69)

**ingenuity** (in jə **n$\overline{oo}$** ə tē) *n.* skill or cleverness used to solve problems (p. 125)

**ingratiate** (in **grā** shē āt) *v.* gain approval for yourself by doing or saying things others like (p. 53)

**inkling** (**ingk** ling) *n.* clue, idea (p. 32)

**innovation** (i nə **vā** shən) *n.* invention, new device (p. 106)

**inscribed** (in **skrībd**) *v.* written or cut into a surface (p. 165)

**ironic** (ī **ron** ik) *adj.* the opposite of what someone might expect (p. 82)

# L

**lit** (lit) *v.* left very quickly (p. 9)

**lopsided** (**lop** sī dəd) *adj.* uneven (p. 131)

**ludicrous** (**l$\overline{oo}$** də krus) *adj.* ridiculous, crazy (p. 104)

# M

**maliciously** (mə **li** shus lē) *adv.* wanting to cause hurt, pain, or suffering (p. 171)

**maneuver** (mə **n$\overline{oo}$** vər) *v.* to move carefully and skillfully (p. 28)

**millennium** (mə **le** nē əm) *n.* period of one thousand years (p. 125)

**misery** (**mi** zə rē) *n.* extreme pain or suffering (p. 4)

**monitored** (**mo** nə tərd) *v.* checked, kept track of (p. 34)

# Glossary

**munitions** (myu **ni** shənz) *n.* weapons used in war (p. 152)

## N

**negotiated** (ni **gō** shē **ā** təd) *v.* got over, through, or around something successfully (p. 50)

**nutrition** (no͞o **tri** shən) *n.* food that helps keep us healthy (p. 82)

**nymph** (nimf) *n.* female spirit who lives in the forest (p. 174)

## O

**obedient** (ō **be** dē ənt) *adj.* following the rules, doing what one is told (p. 16)

## P

**pall** (pawl) *v.* become dull or unpleasant (p. 53)

**parasite** (**pa** rə sīt) *n.* an animal or plant that lives on and gets food from another animal or plant (p. 116)

**pathologist** (pə **tho** lə jist) *n.* a doctor who examines bodies to find the cause of death (p. 158)

**pesticides** (**pes** ti sīdz) *n.* chemicals used to kill insects (p. 117)

**pilgrimages** (**pil** gri mij əz) *n.* journeys to special or holy places (p. 123)

**plush** (plush) *adj.* fancy (p. 100)

**podium** (**pō** dē əm) *n.* a raised platform (p. 41)

**pollination** (pol ə **nā** shun) *n.* moving plant pollen from one plant to another so it can reproduce (p. 117)

**pompous** (**pom** pus) *adj.* snobby, stuck-up, self-important (p. 56)

**porch** (porch) *n.* structure at an entrance to a house (p. 178)

**propaganda** (**pro** pə **gan** də) *n.* ideas or statements spread to help a cause or a government (p. 153)

**published** (**puh** blishd) *v.* recorded in a book or magazine (p. 70)

**punctured** (**pungk** chərd) *adj.* had a hole poked with a sharp object (p. 2)

## Q

**quintessentially** (**kwin** ti **sen** chə lē) *adv.* representing perfectly, being the perfect example of something (p. 167)

**quivered** (kwi vərd) *v.* shook (p. 57)

# R

**rage** (rāj) *n.* extreme anger that is hard to control (p. 182)

**reason** (**rē** zən) *v.* think in a logical way (p. 62)

**recognition** (**re** kig **ni** shən) *n.* special notice or attention (p. 28)

**recruited** (ri **krōō** təd) *v.* persuaded someone to join a group (p. 46)

**regiment** (**re** jə mənt) *n.* military unit made up of large groups of soldiers (p. 88)

**rendered** (**ren** dərd) *v.* made, presented, shown (p. 51)

**resistant** (ri **zis** tənt) *adj.* not harmed or affected by (p. 23)

**retrospect** (**re** trə **spekt**) *n.* thinking about the past (p. 146)

**roused** (rowzd) *v.* stirred up (p. 45)

**rudimentary** (**rōō** di **men** tə rē) *adj.* simple, basic, not advanced (p. 86)

# S

**scenario** (sə **ner** ē ō) *n.* description of what could possibly happen (p. 65)

**sedation** (si **dā** shən) *n.* a sleeplike, relaxed state caused by medication (p. 20)

**shards** (shardz) *n.* sharp pieces (p. 137)

**shrouded** (**shrow** dəd) *adj.* covered (p. 58)

**slogans** (**slō** gənz) *n.* mottoes, chants, catchy sayings in support of something (p. 93)

**solemn** (**so** lem) *adj.* serious (p. 141)

**stalks** (stolkz) *v.* walks stiffly or angrily (p. 182)

**strictly** (**strikt** lē) *adv.* completely, only (p. 143)

**strutted** (**stru** təd) *v.* walked in a bold, confident way (p. 10)

**surveyor** *(*sər **vā** ir) *n.* person whose job is to measure and look at an area of land (p. 122)

**susceptible** (sə **sep** tə bəl) *adj.* able to be harmed by (p. 117)

# T

**taut** (tawt) *adj.* very tense (p. 142)

**teeming** (**tē** ming) *adj.* full of, having a lot of, overflowing (p. 4)

**thwarted** (**thwor** təd) *adj.* defeated, stopped (p. 59)

**tiered** (tērd) *adj.* arranged in layers (p. 178)

**tiers** (tērz) *n.* rows or layers (p. 80)

**tilt** (tilt) *n.* a slant, an upward or downward direction (p. 11)

**transcended** (tran **sen** dəd) *v.* rose above or went beyond (p. 148)

**transplant** (trans **plant**) *v.* to put a body part from one person into another person by operating (p. 21)

# Glossary

**traverse** (tra vers) *v.* travel across or through (p. 26)

**trepidation** (**tre** pi **dā** shən) *n.* feeling of fear (p. 170)

**triggering** (**tri** gər ing) *v.* setting off, starting something (p. 128)

**tumor** (**tōō** mər) *n.* a growth or a mass in the body that is not normal (p. 75)

**tumultuously** (tə **mul** chōō us lē) *adv.* loudly, wildly (p. 170)

**tycoon** (tī **kōōn**) *n.* a wealthy and powerful person in business (p. 110)

# U

**unconventional** (**un** kən **ven** chən əl) *adj.* not traditional or usual (p. 166)

**unkempt** (un **kemt**) *adj.* messy (p. 131)

# V

**vindicated** (**vin** də **kā** təd) *adj.* proved to be correct (p. 161)

**violated** (**vī** ə **lāt** əd) *v.* did something that isn't allowed (p. 88)

# W

**winching** (**win** ching) *v.* pulling very slowly and with effort (p. 14)

# Y

**yelp** (yelp) *n.* a quick, high-pitched yell (p. 14)

# Acknowledgments

WRINGER by Jerry Spinelli. Text copyright © 1997 by Jerry Spinelli. Used by permission of HarperCollins Publishers.

"The Ideal Candidate", "Latch Undone", "Hiring Flora", from PURE DEAD MAGIC by Debi Gliori, copyright © 2001 by Debi Gliori. Used by permission of Alfred A. Knopf, an imprint of Random House Children's Books, a division of Random House, Inc.

From SOLDIER'S HEART: BEING THE STORY OF THE ENLISTMENT AND DUE SERVICE OF THE BOY CHARLEY GODDARD IN THE FIRST MINNESOTA VOLUNTEERS A NOVEL OF THE CIVIL WAR by Gary Paulsen, copyright © 1998 by Gary Paulsen. Used by permission of Delacorte Press, an imprint of Random House Children's Books, a division of Random House, Inc.

[UK:] From SOLDIER'S HEART by Gary Paulsen, published by Delacorte Press, an imprint of Random House Children's Books, a division of Random House, Inc. Text copyright © 2000 Gary Paulsen.

From SAVVY by Ingrid Law, copyright © 2008 by Ingrid Law. Used by permission of Dial Books for Young Readers, A Division of Penguin Young Readers Group, A Member of Penguin Group (USA) Inc., 345 Hudson Street, New York, NY 10014. All rights reserved.

[UK:] From SAVVY by Ingrid Law (pages 1–14, 17–20, 27–30, 35), published in the United States of America by Dial Books for Young Readers, a Division of Penguin Young Readers Group, 2008. Reproduced by permission of Penguin Books Ltd.

"A Remarkable Adventure." Text copyright © 1990 by Jack Prelutsky. Used by permission of HarperCollins Publishers.

"Simile: Willow and Ginkgo" from IT DOESN'T ALWAYS HAVE TO RHYME by Eve Merriam. Copyright © 1964, 1992 Eve Merriam. All Rights Reserved. Used by permission of Marian Reiner.

"Oranges" from NEW AND SELECTED POEMS © 1995 by Gary Soto. Used with permission of Chronicle Books LLC, San Francisco. Visit Chroniclebooks.com.

"Caged Bird", copyright © 1983 by Maya Angelou, from SHAKER, WHY DON'T YOU SING? by Maya Angelou. Used by permission of Random House, Inc.

# Credits

COVER (t) Jack Hollingsworth/Photodisc/Getty Images; (c) Alan Schein/Alamy; (b) Peter Adams/Digital Vision/Getty Images; (bl) Corbis - All Rights Reserved; 1 (l r) Photodisc/Getty Images; 1 (t) Ingram Publishing/SuperStock; 1 (b) Anna Williams/Stockbyte/Getty Images; 1 (b) M. Constantini/PhotoAlto; 1 (bkgd) Anatoly Vartanov/Alamy; 2 Photodisc/Getty Images; 3 (t) Photodisc/Getty Images; 3 (b) M. Constantini/PhotoAlto; 4 Photodisc/Getty Images; 5 (t) Ingram Publishing/SuperStock; 5 (bkgd) Anatoly Vartanov/Alamy; 7 (b) Anna Williams/Stockbyte/Getty Images; 7 (b) Ingram Publishing/SuperStock; 7 (bkgd) Alan Schein/Alamy; 9 (t) Ingram Publishing/SuperStock; 9 (bkgd) Alan Schein/Alamy; 10 11 Alan Schein/Alamy; 13 (l r) Photodisc/Getty Images; 13 (b) Alexey Stiop/Alamy; 13 (b) Anna Williams/Stockbyte/Getty Images; 13 (bkgd) Ingram Publishing/SuperStock; 15 Photodisc/Getty Images; 16 Alexey Stiop/Alamy; 17 (t) Photodisc/Getty Images; 17 (b) Alexey Stiop/Alamy; 19 (t) CDC/Janice Haney Carr; 19 (c) Getty Images/Image Source; 19 (b) Anna Williams/Stockbyte/Getty Images; 21 Getty Images/Image Source; 22 23 CDC/Janice Haney Carr; 25 (t) Zero Creatives/Getty Images; 25 (c) Bob Hallinen/Anchorage Daily News/MCT via Getty Images; 25 (b) Anna Williams/Stockbyte/Getty Images; 25 (bl) Chris Hackett/Getty Images; 25 Author's Image/PunchStock; 27 (l) Zero Creatives/Getty Images; 27 (r) Author's Image/PunchStock; 28 Chris Hackett/Getty Images; 29 Bob Hallinen/Anchorage Daily News/MCT via Getty Images; 31 (l) NASA, Steve Lee University of Colorado, Jim Bell Cornell University; 31 (r) NASA/JPL-Caltech/University of Arizona/Texas A&M University; 31 (b) Anna Williams/Stockbyte/Getty Images; 31 (bkgd) NASA/JPL; 33 NASA/JPL; 34 NASA, Steve Lee University of Colorado, Jim Bell Cornell University; 35 NASA/JPL-Caltech/University of Arizona/Texas A&M University; 37 (t) HultonArchive/Hulton Royals Collection/Getty Images; 37 (tr) Lauren Burke/Lifesize/Getty Images; 37 (b) Anna Williams/Stockbyte/Getty Images; 37 (b) Corbis - All Rights Reserved; 37 (bc) Don Farrall/Getty Images; 39 (t) HultonArchive/Illustrated London News/Getty Images; 39 (b) Corbis - All Rights Reserved; 40 Don Farrall/Getty Images; 41 Lauren Burke/Lifesize/Getty Images; 43 (r) Annabelle Breakey/Digital Vision/Getty Images; 43 (b) Anna Williams/Stockbyte/Getty Images; 44 Annabelle Breakey/Digital Vision/Getty Images; 47 Steve Allen/Brand X Pictures; 49 (r) Tracy Montana/PhotoLink/Getty Images; 49 (b) Anna Williams/Stockbyte/Getty Images; 51 Tracy Montana/PhotoLink/Getty Images; 53 Ingram Publishing; 55 (l) Gary S Chapman/Photographer's Choice RF/Getty Images; 55 (r) Royalty-Free/Corbis; 55 (b) Anna Williams/Stockbyte/Getty Images; 56 Gary S Chapman/Photographer's Choice RF/Getty Images; 57 Royalty-Free/Corbis; 59 Ewen Charlton/Getty Images; 61 (t) Ben Hider/Getty Images Entertainment/Getty Images; 61 (c) Glenn Mitsui/Getty Images; 61 (b) Anna Williams/Stockbyte/Getty Images; 61 (b) Chad Baker/Getty Images; 62 Glenn Mitsui/Getty Images; 63 (t) Ben Hider/Getty Images Entertainment/Getty Images; 63 (b) Chad Baker/Getty Images; 65 Chad Baker/Getty Images; 67 (l) MUSTAFA OZER/AFP/Getty Images; 67 (b) Anna Williams/Stockbyte/Getty Images; 67 (bkgd) Ingram Publishing; 69 (r) MUSTAFA OZER/AFP/Getty Images; 69 (b) Ingram Publishing; 70 71 Ingram Publishing; 73 (l c) New York Public Library/Photo Researchers, Inc.; 73 (b) Anna Williams/Stockbyte/Getty Images; 73 (b) Keith R. Porter/Photo Researchers, Inc.; 75 (t) New York Public Library/Photo Researchers, Inc.; 75 (b) Keith R. Porter/Photo Researchers, Inc.; 76 77 Keith R. Porter/Photo Researchers, Inc.; 79 (c) DEA/G. DAGLI ORTI/De Agostini Picture Library/Getty Images; 79 (b) Anna Williams/Stockbyte/Getty Images; 79 (b) Ingram Publishing; 81 (t) DEA/G. DAGLI ORTI/De Agostini Picture Library/Getty Images; 81 (b) Ingram Publishing; 83 Ingram Publishing; 85 (l) McGraw-Hill Companies, Inc. Bredt Covitz, photographer; 85 (t) Library of Congress, Prints & Photographs Division [LC-USZC4-5592]; 85 (r) Ingram Publishing/Alamy; 85 (b) Anna Williams/Stockbyte/Getty Images; 87 Ingram Publishing/Alamy; 89 McGraw-Hill Companies, Inc. Bredt Covitz, photographer; 91 (l) C. Borland/PhotoLink/Getty Images; 91 (t) Library of Congress, Prints & Photographs Division [LC-USZC4-5592]; 91 (b) Anna Williams/Stockbyte/Getty Images; 95 C. Borland/PhotoLink/Getty Images; 97 (l) CMCD/Getty Images; 97 (t) Library of Congress, Prints & Photographs Division [LC-USZC4-5592]; 97 (r) Burke/Triolo/Brand X Pictures/Jupiterimages; 97 (b) Anna Williams/Stockbyte/Getty Images; 101 (l) CMCD/Getty Images; 101 (r) Burke/Triolo/Brand X Pictures/Jupiterimages; 103 (l) Ingram Publishing/Fotosearch; 103 (r) Pixtal/age fotostock; 103 (b) Anna Williams/Stockbyte/Getty Images; 103 (bkgd) David Henderson/OJO Images/Getty Images; 105 (t) Pixtal/age fotostock; 105 (b) David Henderson/OJO Images/Getty Images; 107 Ingram Publishing/Fotosearch; 109 (l) I. Rozenbaum & F. Cirou/PhotoAlto; 109 (t) Bettmann/Corbis; 109 (r) Comstock Images/Getty Images; 109 (b) Anna Williams/Stockbyte/Getty Images; 109 (b) McGraw-Hill Companies, Inc. Mark Steinmetz, photographer; 111 (t) Bettmann/Corbis; 111 (b) McGraw-Hill Companies, Inc. Mark Steinmetz, photographer; 112 I. Rozenbaum & F. Cirou/PhotoAlto; 113 (t) Comstock Images/Getty Images; 113 (b) McGraw-Hill Companies, Inc. Mark Steinmetz, photographer; 115 (l) Stockbyte/Getty Images; 115 (r) Foodcollection; 115 (b) Anna Williams/Stockbyte/Getty Images; 115 (b) Comstock/PunchStock; 115 (bkgd) Creatas Images/PictureQuest; 117 (t) Stockbyte/Getty Images; 117 (b) Comstock/PunchStock; 118 Foodcollection; 119 Creatas Images/PictureQuest; 121 (l) image100/Corbis; 121 (t) Peter Adams/Getty Images; 121 (c) Ingram Publishing; 121 (b) Aaron Roeth Photography; 121 (b) Anna Williams/Stockbyte/Getty Images; 123 Peter Adams/Getty Images; 124 Aaron Roeth Photography; 125 (l) image100/Corbis; 125 (r) Aaron Roeth Photography; 127 (t) Ingram Publishing/SuperStock; 127 (b) Anna Williams/Stockbyte/Getty Images; 130 Ingram Publishing/SuperStock; 133 (r) Brand X Pictures/PunchStock; 133 (b) Anna Williams/Stockbyte/Getty Images; 137 Brand X Pictures/PunchStock; 139 (t) Douglas Pulsipher/Alamy; 139 (b) Anna Williams/Stockbyte/Getty Images; 143 Douglas Pulsipher/Alamy; 145 (l) Alberto E. Rodriguez/Getty Images Entertainment/Getty Images; 145 (t) Nick Koudis/Getty Images; 145 (r) JoeFox/Alamy; 145 (b) Anna Williams/Stockbyte/Getty Images; 145 (b) ArcadeImages/Alamy; 147 (t) Alberto E. Rodriguez/Getty Images Entertainment/Getty Images; 147 (b) ArcadeImages/Alamy; 148 JoeFox/Alamy; 149 Nick Koudis/Getty Images; 151 (l) Gary Gladstone/Creatas/PunchStock; 151 (c) MPI/Archive Photos/Getty Images; 151 (r) Library of Congress Prints & Photographs Division [LC-USE6-D-004083]; 151 (b) Anna Williams/Stockbyte/Getty Images; 153 (l) Library of Congress Prints & Photographs Division [LC-USE6-D-004083]; 153 (r) MPI/Archive Photos/Getty Images; 155 Gary Gladstone/Creatas/Jupiterimages; 157 (l) Brand X Pictures/PunchStock; 157 (t) NANCY KEDERSHA/UCLA/Science Photo Library/Getty Images; 157 (r) Library of Congress Prints and Photographs Division [LC-USZ62-60242]; 157 (b) Anna Williams/Stockbyte/Getty Images; 159 (t) Library of Congress Prints and Photographs Division [LC-USZ62-60242]; 159 (b) NANCY KEDERSHA/UCLA/Science Photo Library/Getty Images; 160 NANCY KEDERSHA/UCLA/Science Photo Library/Getty Images; 161 (t) Brand X Pictures/PunchStock; 161 (b) NANCY KEDERSHA/UCLA/Science Photo Library/Getty Images; 163 (l) Nice One Productions/Corbis; 163 (r) Purestock/SuperStock; 163 (b) Alan SCHEIN/Alamy; 163 (b) Anna Williams/Stockbyte/Getty Images; 165 (t) Purestock/SuperStock; 165 (b) Alan SCHEIN/Alamy; 166 Alan SCHEIN/Alamy; 167 (t) Nice One Productions/Corbis; 167 (b) Alan SCHEIN/Alamy; 169 (r) McGraw-Hill Companies Inc., Ken Karp, photographer; 169 (b) Anna Williams/Stockbyte/Getty Images; 173 (l) Digital Vision/Getty Images; 173 (t) Photographer's Choice/Getty Images; 173 (r) View Stock/Getty Images; 173 (b) Anna Williams/Stockbyte/Getty Images; 174 Photographer's Choice/Getty Images; 174–175 Digital Vision/Getty Images; 175 View Stock/Getty Images; 177 (l) Brand X Pictures/PunchStock; 177 (r) Foodcollection; 177 (b) Anna Williams/Stockbyte/Getty Images; 179 Foodcollection; 181 Anna Williams/Stockbyte/Getty Images.